Threads of Light

Threads of Light

A YOGA TAPESTRY

By

Slava Kolpakov

Epigraph Books

Rhinebeck, New York

ISBN-978-1-944037-58-1
E-Book ISBN-978-1-944037-60-4

Library of Congress Control Number: 2016963718

Cover design by Rebecca Gray
Interior design by Rebecca Gray
www.amara-designs.com

Slava Kolpakov
www.threadsoflightbook.com
Email: slavasurya@aol.com

Special discounts are available on quantity purchases. For details, contact the publisher at the above listed address. U.S. trade bookstores and wholesalers: **Please contact Slava Kolpakov** Tel: (781) 296-6249; or email slavasurya@aol.com

Epigraph Books
22 East Market Street, Suite 304
Rhinebeck, NY 12572
(845) 876-4861
www.epigraphs.com

Acknowledgements

First and foremost, I am most grateful to my wonderful wife, *Theresa*, for her constant support and inspiration.

I am deeply indebted to my spiritual teacher *Sri Swami Satchidananda* for his extensive spiritual legacy he left us all with, for his wit and humor, and his depth of insight.

Swami Asokananda, a dear friend and teacher, has been a guiding light and inspiration since my first days of teaching yoga in New York City. I am so grateful for your wisdom and patience, and your profound insight into yogic philosophy.

Natasha Rizopoulos – thank you for keeping it real, for being an authentic human being, and for your friendship.

Rebecca Gray – thank you for creativity, honesty, and patience, as well as your interest and eagerness to examine every spiritual idea, especially if it concerns Bhakti Yoga.

I have been blessed to be surrounded by like-minded yogis, and I thank all of my friends, fellow yoga teachers, healers, and bodyworkers for their presence in my life.

I would also like to extend a special thread of gratitude to my friend *Afkham Salie* at *L'Aroma Café*, and *John* and *Judith* at *Judith's Kitchen* in West Newton, MA, for creating their cozy café ambiance where I would write and compile these stories.

Table of Contents

Introduction

A myriad of stars punctured the black sky. The shine of the stars was reflected in the eyes of my three friends sitting in front of me, our silence occasionally interrupted by a distant warning horn from a riverboat. I was sitting on a mountaintop in the twilight of Siberian summer.

After a few minutes of silence: *"Let your whole body relax where it is. Take another long breath."* I observed myself uttering something along those lines. *"Close your eyes, and imagine that your whole body is made out of brilliant light. Let every breath you take bring that light inside your body..."*

The year was 1988. I was twelve. It was a typical summer night in Siberia, where I spent my childhood. I had no formal meditation training. Yet I practiced and offered informal meditation instruction since I was about ten.

Despite living in Soviet Russia, where religious and spiritual beliefs were taboo at the time, my parents practiced yoga, Tai-Chi, studied Eastern philosophy, followed a healthy diet, and observed other practices considered eccentric in that culture. I remember my father fasting for days on water on a regular monthly basis, making Kombucha tea and Rejuvelac drink at home, studying Qi Gong breathing exercises, and running to a hole in the ice in the Yenisey river to dump a bucket of freezing water over his head in the middle of Siberian winter as our neighbors looked on in bewilderment and disbelief. Even as a child, I knew these lifestyle practices were not typical, and they fascinated me, although it would take me a while to integrate yoga into my own lifestyle as an adult.

This book is a collection of writings, stories, and insights from my practice of yoga. A few of these stories have been inspired by those distant days of learning and meditating about the nature of the universe in Siberia. Life was slower-paced and less hurried there. It was easier to pause and connect to the all-pervading Universal Consciousness with little distraction and far away from the rest of the world.

The neighborhoods in my home city, Krasnoyarsk, stretch along the Yenisey river, one of the largest rivers in Russia. The Sayan mountains surrounding the city are visible in every direction. I remember running away from my gymnastics class one afternoon with a couple of friends. We were about ten or eleven years old, and not fond of our instructor who used to force-stretch us into various split positions.

On this day, we conspired to skip the class and do something fun outside. *"How about heading into the mountains,"* I suggested and pointed to the closest range of bluish mountain silhouettes. We walked through the city streets, neighborhood after neighborhood, for almost an hour. There was no traffic on the roads in those days. Few people owned cars in Soviet Russia. The mountains did not seem to get any closer. With their view being our only compass, we were getting into unknown territory. Starting to feel uneasy and lost, we decided to turn back. Perhaps, we should take a bus next time, we decided. Luckily, we found our way back. But we had fun along the way discussing what we could possibly discover in the mountains, what trees we would climb, and if we would see a brown bear.

Although we did not reach our destination that day, the river and the mountains had always been the draw for people to spend time in nature. We would take a bus, or a river tram, up or down the river to a remote village for fishing, swimming, hiking, cave-climbing, and meditating in the woods. My parents headed into the woods almost every weekend.

My father belonged to an underground martial arts club which was operated by his close friend from the Army. They served in the Soviet Army together on the border of Russia and Japan patrolling the numerous coastal islands, a place of high tension between the two countries, each claiming their ownership over the highly coveted fishing territories. My father's friend was a martial arts expert, and was responsible for providing the hand-to-hand combat training to Russian soldiers. Growing up, I heard many stories about their army experiences, which included dealing with bad weather, bad generals, bad food, and innumerable conflicts and altercations with the Japanese soldiers and their staged 'peaceful' combat matches. The Russians would usually lose. But my father's friend never lost a single match.

Once back in the city, the friend found a space for a martial arts gym. The operation had to be kept secret because private enterprises were banned by the communist state. However, many military and police officers became members of the club, to practice and connect with like-minded people, all while maintaining the façade of a regular apartment. My father taught a yoga class there twice a week. It was very informal and not a flow class as most classes in America these days. Instead, it was a workshop-style class with detailed explanations of breathing and energy movement within each pose, often followed by a discussion after each pose. Many yoga poses were often practiced multiple times to notice and feel their different aspects and arising sensations.

I visited the club many times, but never actually participated in a full yoga class. Instead, I would take the Kung Fu and Qi Gong classes taught by our family's friend, or else hang out in the weights room climbing a rock-climbing wall, throwing Ninja stars at a darts target, or doing handstands.

The most impressive aspect of the club was the friendly atmosphere and a strong sense of community. It seemed that even such taboo subjects as religion and spirituality were open to discussion among the members. There was tremendous interest in Eastern philosophy and spirituality and simultaneously a very limited access to any spiritual literature and teachings. I remember leafing through a bunch of Hungarian books on yoga that somehow my father got his hands on. There was always time for meditation after each class, followed by discussion about the nature of consciousness and our life's purpose.

Often, the meditation sessions were lead by my father or other experienced practitioners. This is where I got my idea for it and developed my early thirst for spiritual practices.

Despite being steeped in that early exposure to yoga, this book includes my more recent inquiries and observations inspired by various teachers and personal meditations while living in America. In 2000, I wandered the streets of New York City and stumbled upon Integral Yoga Institute on 13th Street near Greenwich Village. At the time, I was searching for a good path in life, feeling lost, and making a concerted effort to succeed as an actor in New York, on stage and in film. Integral Yoga Institute felt like home, instantly familiar, and reminiscent of my early experiences at the club in Russia.

I met Swami Satchidananda, the founder of Integral Yoga, and, impressed with Swamiji's depth of spirit, authenticity, sense of humor, and ability to communicate complex spiritual truths in a simple disarming way, spent the next several years studying yoga with the help of his senior instructors at the Institute. I started teaching yoga classes in 2002 and made it my practice to share spiritual insights and inspiring stories in my yoga classes.

Many stories and insights in this book have been written as yoga class themes, and therefore may feel conversational or even instructional. Often, I would write down an inspiring thought on a piece of paper, or jot down a few lines on a napkin for reference right before teaching a class. I would write the way I intended to speak to my students. The stories are intended to *stop the world* in the words of Carlos

Castaneda[1] – to notice the underlying reality beneath the day-to-day hustle and bustle of our minds, to make us pause, ponder, and wonder, and to seek wisdom in the smallest and simplest things. I recommend not rushing through the pages, but sitting with each story for a moment. It may evoke a sense of recognition or spark a new take on an existing perspective.

The stories are arranged in a particular order to build upon one another, like threads of a tapestry, complementing each other and ultimately making up a single but multi-faceted whole. This whole is the understanding of yoga: what it is as a philosophy, as a science, and as a practice.

The reader may be familiar with *The Yoga Sutras of Patanjali*,[2] a comprehensive and definitive guide on yoga. *Threads of Light* is by no means a representation or interpretation of the Sutras. Some entries in this collection of stories may correlate and resemble the Sutras. However, it is not my intent to reproduce the Sutras in a different light or see them in a different perspective. The Yoga Sutras are a work of art of a supremely clear-minded yogi, and, in my opinion, cannot be replicated, but only elucidated and contemplated upon, as many existing books of commentaries attempt to do. Instead, the stories in this book are sparks of insight, observations, and small kernels of wisdom from various spiritual teachings. My hope is that the reader will gain a broader understanding of yoga for personal development and of the role of yoga in our culture.

1.) In *The Teachings of Don Juan* by Carlos Castaneda; the shaman Don Juan attempts to "awaken" the author from the everyday reality into the reality of the dreams.

PART 1:
Yoga

"*Story is integral to human life. It is one of the paramount ways in which humans make sense of lived experience.*"
(*P.J. Lewis*)[3]

Yoga

I was never attracted to yoga for its physical benefits. My view of yoga as a child was that of a peculiar system of boring exercises performed by older people with mediocre physical abilities. Every morning I watched my father practice yoga asanas that presented a minimal challenge to me. He would spend minutes holding a Cobra pose, a Shoulder-stand, or a forward bend, after which he would sit still expanding his abdomen and ribcage with deep breaths. I could see nothing fun or interesting about that procedure.

Instead, I was fascinated by the impossible feats of the human body. My heroes were athletes like the Olympian runner Carl Lewis, and the Soviet wrestler Alexander Karelin. In my early childish imagination, I entertained thoughts of becoming a ninja or a Shaolin monk. Since six years of age I attended a gymnastics class, and by the time I was ten, I could do back-flips, walk on my hands, jump into a split, and run up and flip back off a wall. Doing a Cobra pose presented no challenge.

However, there was another dimension of yoga that I was exposed to through my father. After his morning practice, he was always in a good mood and full of energy. As stressful as his life was, he never showed any stress, but instead emanated peace, self-control, and focus.

Years later, as I searched for meaning in my own life, it was that jovial memory of my father that drew me to seek yoga for its internal benefits. What is yoga? How does one find inner peace? Can people be really happy? What is happiness? These were the questions swirling in my mind as I made a life-long commitment to embark on my own yoga journey.

The Secret Goal of Yoga:
How Yoga Practice Changes Your Life

A giant oak tree grows from a single seed. How long does it take to reach its full height? Dozens, maybe hundreds of years.

Like a seed planted long ago, the tradition of yoga germinated, sprouted, and has grown into a global tree, a widely popular practice with many branches and styles.

As a practical system, yoga was developed over five thousand years ago. Why did it take this long to become popular? There have been many yogis throughout history, but never was yoga so widespread as it is today.

Perhaps, the teachings have become more available through the use of digital technology, and instant access to information online. In the past, a student had to be pre-qualified to study with a master. Nowadays, not only can anybody practice yoga but they can also become a yoga teacher. It's now available to all.

Ancient yogis recognized powerful effects of this practice on an individual. It transforms and heals. It enlightens and transcends. It is a vehicle for transformation and growth.

They also recognized how yoga can change people as a whole, as a culture. It can be a vehicle for societal and cultural change, or even a cultural evolution.

As a service to the world, the *Rishis* of the past sent out a wish into the future (a mental projection) that "whenever the planet needs the ancient wisdom of yoga, it will re-surface to as much popularity as needed."

The need is here and now. The world needs the wisdom of yoga. Why? What is so special about yoga? What did the ancient yogis foresee?

They saw Ego. A huge ego, growing into billions of faces and invading hundreds of cultures. The ego, or the sense of separateness, is an essential part of the mind. It places us in the infamous human predicament: ensuring our physical and mental safety, but robbing us of the continual experience of inner peace.

As a protective mechanism, the ego continuously strengthens itself through physical training of the body, conditioning and education of the mind, securing a 'comfortable' place in the world socially and financially, and so on. Basically, the ego always looks out for itself, even at the expense of others.

When dealing with other egos, there may be conflict. If unregulated, conflict may grow into war. History has shown how prevalent wars have been in 'solving' problems of the ego.

However, when dealing with the natural world, which has little or no ego and typically doesn't consciously wage war, there is consistent, on-going abuse, overuse, and destruction.

As a conscious human being living in today's world, you already know the damage caused by the constant onslaught of human ego-driven activity on our precious planet.

This is where yoga comes in. But what does yoga have to do with nature and the ego? Well, everything, really.

What is yoga, anyway? Union. Union of everything: body, breath, mind, inner self, and every other living and non-living thing in the entire existence: rocks, plants, animals, and other human beings.

Yoga is a realization that there is oneness behind everything and this Oneness is who you are. It is inexplicable in words or thoughts, but one feels it anyway, when, suddenly but often enough, one peeks beyond the mind's constant chattering.

This experience of oneness, of yoga, of lasting inner peace and happiness, is the opposite of Ego, the sense of separateness.

In fact, yoga, and absolute happiness, are experienced only when the ego is clear, or, to use the language of yoga, purified. Once the ego is pure, yoga happens naturally.

This view of yoga may seem unexpected for many modern yoga class participants due to its current trend toward the physical, but, as a science and a practical system, yoga primarily deals with the mind. It may begin with the physical conditioning of the body - postures and sequences to gain physical control, but all to get a handle on the mind. According to yogic wisdom, to control the mind perfectly is the most difficult task in the Universe.

The body is much easier to control. Gradually, the transition is made from the physical to the subtle energetic and mental exercises.

So what about yoga's secret goal?

Imagine what would happen if large numbers of people had an authentic experience of yoga. Imagine if people could sustain ego-less existence for periods of time long enough to feel compassion for all other beings on Earth. As yogis, awake to our inner nature and in union with our environment, ever conscious of the One essence behind all, we realize that we are inseparable from Mother Earth.

The purpose, or goal, of yoga becomes our purpose in life. We realize that it is our inherent duty to take care of our planet and all its creatures, to live in harmony, as a family, as brothers and sisters, with all, regardless of our cultural backgrounds, color of our skin, our religious beliefs, or societal status. As yogis, we become ecology-warriors, and messengers of Peace. We realize that we are the caretaker-species; and that is why we have a complex mind and the energy for this grand task. We naturally dedicate our lives to alleviate the suffering of others, create peace in the world, raise our common consciousness, and awaken others to their true nature and the unity between all life.

So this is the seldom-told secret about yoga: its goal is to bring about change in the world – global transformation of consciousness. This is what has been projected by the great *Rishis* of the past as a means to save our precious Mother Earth and learn to live in harmony and love.

Why is this a secret? Perhaps, 'hidden' or 'unapparent' may be better words. It is unapparent about yoga that it has such a deep transformational effect on one's consciousness. Often, yoga comes into one's life through the back-door of the ego. People are usually attracted to yoga because of the ego. These days, the common reasons for starting a yoga practice range from getting more flexible, to meeting a cute partner in class, to getting a "yoga-butt." Enlightenment and cultural transformation are usually not on that list.

Thus, the ego plays a crucial role in one's path to self-discovery and ego-purification. With regular practice of Love for the body, mind, inner heart, and the planet, you as a yoga practitioner transform your life to become a real yogi in the original sense of the word. A yogi is a self-realized being in harmony with the their inner self and the world around them.

Meaning of Life

What is the meaning of life? We have all asked this question. Wise men and women, clear-minded thinkers and writers, and spiritual beacons like Jesus, the Buddha, Mohammed, Dalai Lama, Mother Teresa, and Gandhi offered their guidance to our questions and had all shed light on life and our role in it.

We know that life is about Love, and personal evolution, and about giving because we cannot take anything with us into the after-life. The following story, adopted from the writings by a Unitarian minister Robert Fulghum,[4] illustrates my favorite way to understand the purpose of life.

Once, a young man wanted to know the meaning of life. He searched everywhere: in books, in people, and within his own mind. One day he went to hear a wise man speak. At the end of the lecture, the teacher asked if anyone had questions. The seeker stood up and asked, "Sir, could you tell me the meaning of life?"

The audience smiled at the eternal question and began assembling their belongings to leave, but the wise man stopped them. "Wait," he said. "This is a very good question and I have the answer right here in my bag." The teacher reached into his bag and pulled out a small mirror. He caught light with the mirror and directed a beam of light toward the young man.

"Do you see this beam of light?" he asked. "Well, you see, because I am here, I can shine this light into places that it could

not go without me. I become a vehicle for light. I can catch it with my mirror and deliver it to other places. The purpose of life for all of us is to capture Light, and to take it where it is needed."

Coming to an inspiring yoga class is equivalent to capturing Light. Leave knowing that you are that mirror, and spread the Light.

Lifestyle of a Yogi

What does it mean to lead the lifestyle of a yogi? Attending yoga classes, wearing Lululemon clothing and silk scarves made in India, saying "Namaste" when greeting people. Would that make me a yogi?

While all of the above examples are typical, yoga lifestyle means something entirely different. It has nothing to do with the style of yoga people practice, their style of clothing, the type of work they are involved in, or anything else that is externally imposed by fads and culture.

Yoga lifestyle is about one's internal values: What moves or motivates a person to do what they do.

Yoga lifestyle is also about the process: How one goes about performing their daily actions. One can be an artist, a carpenter, a plumber, a car mechanic, a teacher, or a cop. These external descriptions are like seasons – they are in constant change. They describe a temporary occurrence. Our essence remains the same. Our core values determine who we are and if we are living a yogic lifestyle.

Many years ago, I witnessed the following scene in New York City:

A hot and humid summer afternoon was drawing to a close. The busy sidewalk glistened in the slanted sunrays weaving their way through the tall buildings. A young woman with a baby stroller stopped at a street vendor to buy a bottle of water. For a moment, she let go of the stroller handle as she reached for her wallet to pay. In that moment, the baby stroller started to roll down the sidewalk and toward the speeding traffic.

All of a sudden, a teenage boy darted away from his group of friends across the street and sprinted toward the rolling stroller while dodging cars. His sharp and urgent voice "Watch the baby! Watch the baby!" jerked the young mother's head around. She grasped the invisible air handle realizing what happened, and ran toward the stroller, which was already falling over the edge of the sidewalk and into the hands of the teenage boy.

The mother broke into tears and hugged the boy. The boy smiled and shook his head. His friends across the street started clapping their hands. The street vendor and a couple of other passers-by joined the standing ovation. For a few seconds, the busy street stopped, and celebrated the moment. In those few seconds, a wave of love and gratitude rolled through the crowd. Everyone smiled. We all felt connected. We all felt compassionate toward one another and united in our human condition here on planet Earth, regardless of our background and beliefs.

What moved the young man to sprint through the traffic risking his own life? What moved the young woman to hug the boy? What moved the band of young teenagers to applaud this event?

Many yoga masters and spiritual teachers have defined yoga as *"perfection in action."* A perfect action means *"an action that benefits someone and harms no-one."* It is an action rooted in non-violence and compassion coming from a deep source within. When we are living our life in accordance with this principle, we are living the yogic lifestyle.

Non-violence, which stems from compassion, is thought of as the most important yogic principle. It's called *Ahimsa* in Sanskrit and applies to everything: our actions, words, and thoughts. Gandhi dedicated his life to *Ahimsa*. He was a great yogi and a wonderful example of the yogic lifestyle.

There are four more yogic principles of social conduct: truthfulness, non-stealing, faithfulness, and non-greed. Beginning this practice is not easy, but with steady commitment over time these yogic principles become your choices and the natural extension of the compassionate voice of your inner heart.

The yogic lifestyle is the next step in the evolution of humankind.

Becoming Connected
to the Wisdom of the Body

A yoga class is an opportunity to connect with the wisdom of the body. Once a little girl asked her father: "*Dad, what do you do at work?*"

"*I work at a school where I teach people how to draw.*" He answered.

She looked at him for a moment, confused, and said: "*You mean people forget?*"

For a little girl, it is inconceivable to think that one has to learn how to draw, something she does naturally. Maybe we do forget certain things that are natural to us, like yoga, or meditation, or even enlightenment. We simply forget how to access it. Or, maybe, we pretend to forget. We just play the game of forgetting that we really are enlightened already.

But our bodies hold the knowledge of it. A yoga class is an opportunity to connect with the wisdom of the body. This is a practice of listening, of becoming really sensitive, of becoming a witness. It is a meditation practice.

During your next yoga class, ask yourself once in a while: Where is my body right now? What is my body telling me right now? How far to go? How far to stretch? How much to let go? How much to push? How fully to breathe?

Notice what your body is telling you right now, if it wants to move and align in a certain way.

Becoming Connected
to the Everything in Nature

What if, when we are born, we identify with everything we see, smell, hear, touch, and taste? Instead of identifying with the mind, the thinker and the observer, we would automatically assume that we were the observed: "*Oh, that's who I am*," when looking at the clouds, or the trees, or when feeling the wind on our skin, or when smelling the first smells of breast milk. "*I am the clouds. I am the trees. I am the wind. I am my mother's milk.*"

So the other day, I was sitting on the lawn, trying to feel, see, hear, and identify with all of nature. It was a bonding experience: connecting with the world around. As you look around and hear what you hear and feel what you touch, imagine that it is who you actually are. Every thing that comes into your awareness is nothing but you.

I was probably there for a half hour, when suddenly I felt a few drops of liquid on my head. I smiled, knowing that was bird poop, and thought: *I guess that I am that, too.* The hard part is not to identify only with the good and the beautiful like flowers, birds, and clouds, but also with the regular, the mundane, the bad, and the ugly. To accept all, to welcome all.

To welcome any experience and allow for it to flow is yoga. As mentioned earlier, yoga is about union, the sense of oneness. Through this practice, we realize that our bodies are part of the observable nature. You can observe your body just as you can observe a cloud. And if you get really tuned in and sensitive, you can observe your mind, because the mind is also a part of nature. Just like watching a bird take a bath.

Here is an interesting twist: through this practice, we also realize that our True Self is not the external nature. Our bodies and minds are inseparable from all the natural phenomena, yet at the same time, our True Self is not that. What is our True Self? What are we trying to connect with in our lives? Is there something deeper beyond the body and the mind - beyond the constant changing nature? That's what we are here to discover. Yoga is a path of discovery.

Witnessing The Universal Hum

We sat around a big burning fire in California's Santa Cruz mountains with hundreds of other people and chanted peace songs to the tune of skillful singers, musicians, and their instruments.

We chanted for hours, and the rhythms stayed with us as we went to sleep in our tents. Our chants ended, but the hum of the sounds did not stop. At night, the crickets took over the continuous sound. In the morning, as the crickets quieted, the birds woke up and picked up the chants. It never stopped. It is still here and now: the Universal Hum, or the sound OM as it is referred to in yoga.

God, the Universal Consciousness, manifests as sound. Everything hums and vibrates. Inside and outside our skin. Everything in existence, down to the smallest particle, vibrates and contributes to the Universal Om. We are part of it. In fact, we are It.

Tune in to the hum inside. Notice the breath, the heartbeat, blood flow, nerve signals, muscles pulsing, thoughts flowing.

The more still you become, the more you notice. Witness all of it as a single Hum without fixating on any one sound. The continuity of sound. Even the sharp sounds like a car alarm or a sneeze. They are also part of it, and are real blessings as they bring us immediately into the present moment.

Healing Earth

One summer, while living in San Diego and before moving to Boston, my wife and I decided to travel to Krasnoyarsk, my home city in Siberia. On the way, we planned to stop in Boston, Dublin, Nice, and Moscow; and then come back the same way, and do all of this in a month. It was an unrealistic itinerary. But we did it anyway.

To fight the fatigue, in the beginning of our trip in Boston, we found a clean patch of grass by the Charles River, and spent some time relaxing, breathing, and being in direct contact with the earth.

I read somewhere that being in direct contact with the earth, without the rubber or the plastic of our shoes, has a profound healing effect on our physical and emotional selves. Apparently, just above the ground, there is a layer of negative ions. When our body is in contact with them, they neutralize free radicals. This means that they act as antioxidants, which have been getting so much attention in the healing nutrition field. They fight inflammation, and help reverse many serious health conditions.

After an hour of lounging on the grass in Boston, we felt refreshed, as though a veil of fatigue was lifted, or rather pulled down into the earth. We liked it so much that we decided to connect with the earth this way in every city we visited.

In Dublin, we went to St. Stevens Green; in Nice, we found a park with a waterfall just above the city; in the South of France, we found a beach. We did the same in Moscow. In Siberia, there are so many green areas. We went to my family's summerhouse, connecting with the earth by picking garden berries and greens for our salads.

Yoga is often defined as "a conscious union with the Infinite." The Earth's intelligence is infinite in its power to heal. Consciously connecting with Earth's energy is yoga.

Earth Guardians

Every day should be an Earth Day. We practice yoga, and strengthen our bodies, and sharpen our minds to be Earth Guardians. We should all strive to be in harmony with nature and stand to protect our Mother Earth.

A few years ago, my wife, a fellow teacher, and I drove out far into the desert east of Los Angeles to see a man who lives completely off the land. He has no running water, no electricity, and no phone lines. Just him and the land. He grows food by redirecting water from a natural well.

People know about him, and visit him on occasion. He has been there for over twenty years. Apparently, once homeless in San Francisco, he was given this piece of land by a stranger who used to pass him on the street every day.

After a four-hour drive, we approached his living space. At first, we only saw a collection of rugged boulders in the middle of the desert, forming a giant circle. Then, the top of a teepee poked through the rocks into our view. As we parked our car, and walked closer, we saw no other buildings. A make-shift roofless kitchen stood near the teepee: a long wooden table, a sink, and shelves containing only a few plates and pots. A big fluffy cat sat on the table eyeing us with curiosity. Chickens picked at the dirt inside a wire-fence enclosure that encircled the nearest boulder. The air felt still, dry, and dusty. It smelled of desert sage.

The man came out of the teepee to greet us with a big smile and sparkling eyes. He did not say much, just smiled a lot. His energy was calm and light. When I met him, I thought to myself *"This guy is a real yogi, just like in the olden days in India, the yogis lived with the land, in the forest, in the mountains, perfectly connected to their natural environment, perfectly happy."*

We spent all day there. He showed us his chickens, his art pieces that he built into the rocks, his 'hot tub' built between two boulders, and mountain lion tracks - those left in the sand from the night before and those left a few months ago in the cement by the hot tub.

We talked about living out in the desert. He was happy. He knew the time of day not by the time on the clock but by the direction of the shadows cast off the boulders every day. He loved the land. He protected every plant and animal that shared their home with him. He talked about being a guardian for this land for the time being – not an owner.

One of the most important changes a person experiences on his or her yoga journey is developing a deep connection to all living beings and the natural world. Upon becoming a yogi, you become an Earth Guardian, a protector, an advocate, and a peace warrior for the natural health of our planet.

Caretaker Species:
Why Dogs Don't Live Longer Than People

This is a popular story that circulated the Internet among the animal lovers.

A family had an old dog named Belker who was sick. They called a veterinarian who determined that Belker was dying of cancer, and there were no miracles left for him. The vet offered to perform the euthanasia procedure for the old dog.

The adults thought it would be good for their four-year old son, Shane, to observe the procedure. They felt as though Shane might learn that death is part of life and is natural.

Shane seemed so calm, petting the old dog for the last time, that the adults wondered if he understood what was going on. Within a few moments, Belker slipped away peacefully. The little boy seemed to accept Belker's transition without any difficulty or confusion.

They sat together for a while after Belker's death, wondering aloud about the sad fact that animal lives are shorter than human lives. Shane, who had been listening quietly, chimed in, "I know why."

They all turned to him and what followed was the most comforting explanation: "People have to learn how to be nice all the time. Dogs already know how to do that so they don't have to stay as long."

We should all be more like dogs. Live more simply. Love more generously. Speak more kindly and truthfully.

The lives of dogs, cats, and other animals are more simple than people's lives; they are more instinctual. Sometimes, we may wonder if people are the most intelligent animals or less intelligent in certain ways.

Either way, we have these complex minds – minds that can be beautiful tools, or the most frightening weapons. Minds can heal or destroy. The entire science of yoga developed because of this fact, or this predicament, that we have a mind. It gets crazy, distracted, confused, and arrogant. It takes us out of our True Nature which is Peace and Joy.

Yoga is a way to handle that – to purify the mind, to re-condition the mind to see Love and Beauty, to teach it to focus – and then it becomes that beautiful tool. And with this tool, you can grow and contribute in meaningful ways.

The reason we have these complex minds is not to be the most intelligent or dominant species on our planet, but to be the caretaker species.

Listening

Catalina Island is a mountainous island just off the coast of California. My wife and I hiked for two hours on a winding road to reach the island summit. The road leading up to the top is lined with tall Eucalyptus trees.

That day, strong wind played with tree branches. We walked quietly, listening to the wind and the birds. Then we noticed that the trees were talking.

With the wind, the Eucalyptus create a lot of noise. They screech, crackle, creek, whistle, and toot. Once we noticed it, we kept listening, and this act of listening opened up a whole new world of the present moment. The whole mountainside suddenly woke up and started talking. Everything was talking to every thing else, as if a veil was lifted, and we could see the magical reality.

Being in nature has this effect. We are reminded of our connection to the Earth and become more alive. It doesn't have to happen only when we are in nature. Any time, anywhere, it's possible to become more alive. Just begin the act of listening. Listen for the present moment.

In a yoga class, we learn how to listen to our bodies and learn from that wisdom. We can say that yoga is about listening. Listening is the highest form of yoga. Listening is selfless. Listening is an act of giving. Listening is the source of peace. From real in-the-moment listening, we discover new possibilities.

Relative and Absolute

There are two realities in life.

Nature is the relative reality, or the manifested reality. It is only seemingly real. Look at a tree outside. Now it appears to be a tree. But maybe ten years ago, it was a seed. In ten more years, it may be cut to become firewood. And then it will turn to ashes. So which is it then: a seed, a tree, firewood, or ashes? The law of nature is impermanence, constant change. How can anything impermanent be real? What is real is the consciousness that gives room for all of these changes. That is the Absolute reality. You and I are just like the tree: our bodies are impermanent but our essence is one, eternal, and absolutely real. So let's try to remember to see everything as one essence, as a dance or a play of One Consciousness.

There is a story of a mother who was shocked to learn that her ever-loving, kind and caring son was a hardened criminal in the world outside of their home. No person is one way or another. We are all complex creatures and contain opposite qualities within. Every light has darkness.

It is only within the mind that we assign labels and separate things. We see things that are relative as absolute. Our minds split things into good and bad, painful or pleasant. But all these opposites are there only to serve as a lesson. Even pain and suffering are not real in the Absolute reality, but are lessons in the relative world.

The opposites could not exist without each other. Suffering, despair, ugliness, darkness have an important purpose – they define their opposites. One cannot inhale without first exhaling. Relaxation cannot be without tension. Peaceful mind cannot exist without chaos. How would you know to search for peace if you never experienced chaos?

In Absolute reality, there is no separation. Forgetting this will surely lead to problems. You start seeing differences only. I am different. He is different. And your mind always gets afraid when it sees differences. Different is unknown, and the unknown creates fear. From which comes tension and competition, which causes anger and hatred.

If only all people could get themselves out of this limited view. See the One essence behind all nature. One Consciousness. You are part of the impermanent nature (body and mind) and you are also the One essence (True Self) behind all things. You are the trees, and the clouds, and the hungry children in Africa, and the wealthiest people in America, and the Russian mafia, and the Yogis in the Himalayan caves chanting endless chants for peace and sending beautiful vibrations out to the whole Universe. You are all of that in the Absolute reality.

Controlling the Breath

We often hear that yoga is about breath. What does it mean? How is it that our breath is a major aspect of yoga?

The primary reason is that breath is closely linked with the mind. It reflects the mind. If the mind is agitated, so is the breath; if the mind is still, so is the breath. Yoga is about controlling the mind, and the breath happens to be one of the most wonderful tools for getting the mind under conscious control. Consciously slowing down and deepening your breath causes the mind to slow down.

Another quality of the breath is being always in the moment, as is Absolute reality. There is no time in Absolute reality; there is only now, this moment. If you focus on your breath, totally, completely, you forget all the little problems (or big problems) that may be on your mind. The breath provides us with a porthole into this Absolute reality where time does not exist. The breath provides an opportunity of a mini-retreat from the craziness of mental living.

Simply connect to the continuous flow of your breath when you find yourself losing control, and notice how you become more capable of keeping your mental focus, and taking charge of your emotions. Below is a short example from a yoga student:

Before he started yoga, John had experienced a heart attack. Yoga helped him keep his heart healthy. On one particular day, a driver behind him bumped his van when he was leaving his parking spot. He remembered that often a heart spasm/attack is precipitated by anger. So instead of getting angry, he pulled down his window and started doing the alternate nostril breathing. The other driver gave him a very confused look and left. That made John smile. He does this technique all the time now, especially in traffic. His heart health is much better.

We don't have to do alternate nostril breathing in sticky situations, but what we need is to distract the mind, the ego, from reacting to the seeming problem and toward something else, something positive, in the moment, like the breath. Once we form a habit of focusing on the breath with undivided attention, our mind will not spiral into a negative spin.

Transcending the Ego

I remember a teacher once told the class: *"Yoga is about Death."* Everyone threw their arms up in protest: *"No! No way! Yoga is about Life. It's about being alive, fully alive in the moment."*

Then the teacher said: *"That's true, it is about being alive. But a certain kind of death needs to happen before we can be fully alive."*

He was referring to the death of the ego. Death is a strong way of putting it. A better way of saying this may be that the ego, the sense of self-separateness, has to be transcended, or become less of an obstacle. When there is no ego, we see ourselves as one with everything. We are in union with everything. That is called Yoga.

Once I was hiking on Mount Laguna with a few friends, one of my favorite hiking spots. There's a hike around the Big Laguna Lake. A very peaceful place. There are so few signs of human influence that I inevitably want to sit and meditate. Just sit and be. The energy of that place is palpable. At six thousand feet up, one can still smell the desert, but it's much cooler and there's plenty of green.

On this particular hike, we found a collection of giant boulders overlooking an expansive valley. One could probably see for five or six miles. I asked my friends if we could sit there for a half hour, silently, and just witness the present moment.

As I sat there, I tried to let go of my ego. I tried to forget everything I know. I tried to forget everything I know about myself. I tried to let go of any knowledge I have accumulated, to let go of the idea that I am separate, and that I exist. After a while, it felt as though I wasn't there anymore, as if I was transparent, and I could see all around me. I could see life happening all around: squirrels, birds, the wind. It was a powerful experience of yoga.

Yoga is a sense of oneness, or union, which happens naturally when the mind is paused.

Then what are we doing on yoga mats? How do we experience this oneness on the mat?

A yoga class is important because it's where we can learn about the nature of the mind. We come face to face with our limitations and boundaries. Not only physical but also mental and emotional. We have an opportunity, in a safe environment, to get to know the mind, its restless and scattered nature, and an opportunity to collect that mind, to bring it to focus. After all, that is the goal of yoga, according to the Yoga Sutras and other yogic texts – to learn to control the mind. Yoga is defined in the Sutras, a 2,500-year old text, as "cessation of fluctuations of the mind" (*Yogas Chitta Vrtti Nirodhah*).

Starting with the mind right away is very difficult and can be discouraging. So we begin with something easier – the physical body, making it strong, flexible, and under control. Once that is accomplished, the mind is not such a formidable enemy anymore.

Fire of Purification

I remember a story that was told to me by a good friend from Brazil.

Once, in her neighborhood, there was a big fire. Several houses went up in flames. The fire fighters arrived, but it was too late. Nobody could do anything to stop it. People stood outside and watched their homes being destroyed with pain and sadness.

Nearby, there was a small orchard, which remained untouched by the fire. In a few hours, the orchard trees started to bloom with flowers, caused by the heat of the fire.

The sight of the blooming flowers lifted the heavy feeling of loss and pain. At least for the moment, those tiny blooms broke the downward-spiraling momentum. Their colorful image, the birth of something beautiful, made it easier to see a bigger picture: that there's still beauty and love, that life is still happening, and that life is a cycle. There will be a time for renewal, growth, and abundance.

Fire is symbolic. It hurts. It purifies. What is being purified? Where's the flower tree?

Often, on the path of yoga, our mental house, the ego, is on fire, causing the inner flower to bloom. Our body burns up toxins, our mind burns attachments and selfish tendencies.

In a yoga class, the body and the mind may endure such purification. The body gets rid of toxins, stagnation, and stiffness. The mind is put against its own restless nature. Deep-seated desires, fears, and attachments come up to the surface. Having courage and allowing this cleansing to happen is how you develop inner strength, through which you can deal with many of life's difficulties. Nothing could be frightening to you then. That is real yoga.

Developing Inner Strength

My wife is a dog trainer who employs exclusively positive reinforcement techniques. She says with regard to dog training that *"force is the absence of power."* When a trainer resorts to force, physical or verbal, it always shows their lack of respect for the animal.

The concept of *"Force as the absence of Power"* is a yogic concept. A yogi is an individual with a lot of personal power. This is internal power – power over one's own desires, addictions, harmful habits and tendencies. A yogi develops this power with various yogic practices to strengthen their will and gain control over the mind. A yogi does not showcase their physical force to prove his or her point. A yogi's personal power comes from inner strength.

A powerful person stays calm in rough waters, keeps cool when faced with challenges, and non-reacts when provoked. It takes a lot of internal strength to do all that.

When do we resort to force? When our ego is threatened, and we feel that we have no other way to control or influence the situation or the person.

I am talking about a physical, military, intellectual, or any other kind of force that diminishes the receiver of this force in any way.

The use of force is the ultimate example of the ego's reign within the individual. What do we accomplish by using force?

Our ego may feel superior. Our point is made and we may feel that 'we won.' But what is true winning? Isn't it making the other person understand our way deep down in their heart, to turn them into our ally, or our friend?

True winning is to win someone's heart, or friendship, or understanding. To make them see our own perspective through their eyes. The use of force can never accomplish that. In fact, it accomplishes the exact opposite. We gain an enemy, someone who may have been diminished or intimidated by our show of force, but who would always remember the hurt it caused them. The use of force builds barriers, resentment, and deep underlying conflicts. We don't have to look very far to see many examples of it: the conflict between the American law enforcement and the black community, or the conflict between the Western nations and the Islamic fundamentalists. The use of force whether it's by police, by terrorists, or by Western air strikes leads nowhere – it wins no hearts. It only destroys and deepens the wounds.

What can we learn from it? Power does not come from force. Force is the absence of power. This is an effective mantra to say to yourself when faced with a conflict. Finding an alternative, a positive solution to the conflict, based on mutual understanding and love, is the yogic way.

Real power comes from deep under-standing, or standing under (as in bowing your head, letting go of the ego), and compassion meaning 'common passion.' Taking the time to understand and feel the pain, the emotions, and the underlying motivations behind the other person is the way to real power. When a person feels that you completely understand them, they will reciprocate by trying to understand you too. When they feel that you have given up your ego to listen to their concerns, they will extend their gratitude to you and make concessions for you too. In psychology, it's known as the Principle of Reciprocity. We are all taught from a young age to share, to thank when given something, to reciprocate kindness.

Real power comes from listening, caring, and love.

Becoming a Mystic

A mystic is someone who deals with the unseen, unknown, and inexplicable. Things beyond the physical, or metaphysical, are the realm of the mystic. These are things that are infinite, timeless, and unthinkable.

A yogi is a mystic. The goal of yoga is Self-Realization, also known as enlightenment, or unity with the True Self. Yogis know that the True Self (our true nature) cannot be known through the mind. One has to find another way to reveal the Self.

We can divide all knowledge into three categories: the Known, the Unknown (can be learned), and the Unknowable. The latter is the stuff of the mystic.

The True Self Realization falls into the category of the Unknowable through the mind. The mind cannot comprehend what is beyond the mind. No words or thoughts are able to describe the True Self experience as the words are simply part of the limited mind. A yogi seeks the beyond-the-mind experience.

Seeing the Mystical:
The Moose, The Ram, and Being Present

My wife and I were driving across Massachusetts to visit Kripalu Yoga Center. There were few cars on the road. All of a sudden, we were drawn to a big dark shape on the side of the road. We both immediately thought that it was a man on a horse. As we got nearer, we realized that it was in fact a gigantic Moose.

Standing completely still, he was about twenty feet away from the edge of the road and had an impressive set of antlers.

For those few seconds that we were passing the animal, we couldn't even exclaim in amazement, we were so taken by its powerful presence. In those few seconds, before we could say *'Wow!' 'Holy … !'* or *'What the?!'* we were in a meditative state. Our mind was stilled, stunned, by the powerful presence. There was no mental chattering, no questions, fears, or worries, just pure awareness.

A few years later, we were visiting San Diego. It was June, and half the day was immersed in thick marine fog known as the marine layer, the infamous 'June Gloom.' We decided to get away for a day into the desert. A desert in June is hot with temperatures well above 110 degrees in the day. For that reason, few people visit the desert at that time of year, and it can be a really special quiet and meditative time to be there.

In the morning, we got up at five a.m. to hike one of our favorite trails to a desert oasis. At night, the temperature drops to a cool 85 degrees, and it's back up to 100 by nine a.m., so we wanted to get in a couple of hours of hiking before the heat became intolerable.

Making our way on a winding trail, we noticed fresh sheep scat. Typically, nothing moist looks fresh under the hot desert sun for too long, so my wife commented that it was very recent, possibly left less than an hour ago. We stood quietly, listening to the hot wind gusts, smelling the scents of sage and desert lavender, and looking at the steep rocky canyons full of brown scrub brush, a variety of cactus such as jumping Chollas and prickly pears, Ocotillos, and Chuparosa plants. These plants provide food and shelter for many desert animals. One of them is the rarely seen endangered Desert Bighorn Sheep. Excellent climbers, the bighorns are hard to spot and shy away from people.

As we neared the oasis, we could hear the water trickling in the rocks, and see the stark abundance of greenery among the ubiquitous grey and brown colors. I walked along the trail first with my wife right behind me. All of a sudden, a big grey shape bolted from under a bush in front of me and onto the trail. Both of us froze in mid-stance, our breath caught. It was an old male ram. A grandfather Bighorn. He stood at about five feet tall. Moving his head side to side with his giant curved horns, he stared directly at us, and huffed and stomped his hooves in a way that jolted us from our frozen astonishment. The fear of potentially serious danger set in. My wife whispered *"OK, step back, slowly, and avert your eyes."* We started side-stepping down the trail. The Ram stood his ground for a few seconds, then turned around and scampered up the trail toward the oasis. We turned and headed away from it, not wanting to startle others from a much-needed water source. At this time of year, in the heat of the summer, the sheep do not expect to see people here. We clearly surprised him, and probably scared him as much as he stunned us.

As we made our way back down the trail, we felt exhilarated and excited about this encounter. The moment he sprang from under the bush, our mind was stunned and empty in a zen-like way. This clarity only lasted a few seconds, but felt much longer. Time stopped at the moment of the encounter. The mind was off as if someone turned a switch and stopped all thinking and processing. Only pure awareness remained.

Animals have that power. In Native American tradition, animals are seen as guides and teachers. They come into our lives to show us how to be more connected to Nature. They teach us how to be present.

Connecting with that part of ourselves is Yoga. In fact, it's more yoga than practicing physical postures on the mat. The Moose and the Ram encounters are those magical mystical moments that connect us to the True Self and to all other beings intimately and instantaneously. Yoga poses are designed to do that, as they are tools to access the present moment, but they are not as spontaneous as encounters with Nature.

I encourage you to look for those special moments in your life. Spend more time in nature, and with animals, learning and observing. Forests, mountains, and oceans are sacred temples. Animals are our real teachers. They have the power to instantly clear the veils of our mind and force us to be vibrantly alive in the Now.

Every Moment is Special

Visiting Grass Valley, California, we stayed in a cabin in the woods. Coming up to the cabin at dusk, we came upon a small herd of deer. The animals looked up at us and we locked eyes for a few short seconds. Yet, the moment of connection felt timeless. Infinite. In a moment like that, there is no time. No thoughts.

For a *Jivamukti* (a liberated enlightened being) every moment is that way. When we notice the beauty around us – the moment of seeing it – the deer, the mountains, the waves crashing, the birds flying – we are enlightened. Why does a breath-taking view takes our breath away? That is a spontaneous *Kumbhaka*: breath retention. When every-day busy mind stops, we experience the timeless reality.

The reason we see the beauty outwardly is because we have the beauty within. If it was not inside us already, we would not know what to look for and would not recognize it outside if we saw it.

The beauty is inside us. Every moment can be special. All we need to do is turn inward and notice.

We use the tools available: our senses. Our senses connect with the world around us in this moment only. Our mind drives us away from the moment to analyze what the senses discover.

Sometimes the mind can be used to behold the timeless moment, if we are able to witness the mind without getting caught up in the past or the future. To witness the mind, one must have a strong sense of the inner observer. Can you watch your own thoughts? Who is watching the thoughts?

What Makes Life Special?

We remember certain times in our lives as special moments. Moments we remember forever. We meet old friends and reminisce about the 'good ole' times. Have you thought about what made those times so special?

Whether those special moments were filled with adventure and intensity, or were the most mundane moments, there is one simple similarity: We lived in the present moment.

We remember only those times when we allowed the richness of the outside world to interact fully with all of our senses. We kept ourselves open to the present experience moment by moment. Those experiences get recorded in our memories forever as special moments.

On the other hand, we do not remember when we were lost in thought. We do not remember when we sat and thought about the past or the future. Those times are just bleeps in our memory.

That is one simple truth about life. Our life is not the days we have lived but the days we remember. In other words, our life is the sum total of all present moment living.

Experiencing Innate Sense of Freedom and Inner Peace

I have often defined Yoga as *"a science of how to be happy."* This is not about the kind of happiness when you feel happy today and not so happy tomorrow. I am talking about lasting Happiness that is always present no matter what happens. It's more than Happiness. It's a sense of utmost contentment and inner peace. It's an innate sense of freedom that we all have, that we all seek, and, as the paradox of life would have it, we all are.

I remember an email I once received from my teacher about his cat. His cat passed away and he wrote this beautiful poetic description of their life together. He chose to see his cat as a manifestation or reincarnation of something Divine, like the Divine Mother. He said that his cat was there to teach him how to be in the moment and to remind him to stay connected to Nature.

There is one line I specifically remember from his email: *'All beings, without exception, seek liberation and freedom from bondage. Not only human beings; we all seek the freedom that we already possess.'* This kind of ultimate freedom is known as *Moksha* in yogic philosophy. *Moksha* is the goal of yoga – the experience of total liberation from any kind of suffering. It's a deep visceral knowledge of one's own true nature – experienced on a continual basis moment to moment.

A yoga class is an opportunity to connect with this innate sense of freedom. We often encounter silence, stillness, and peek beyond the hurricane of the mind. First, we face our limitations in a yoga class, not only physical limitations, but also mental and emotional bonds and restlessness.

Our mind understands something through its opposite. We know peace because we also know confusion. We understand happiness because we understand despair and pain. We can understand and experience *Moksha* through its opposite sense of being bound. We understand what it is like to be free when we are limited.

Next time you take a yoga class, notice if you feel more bound and more restless than usual, and look to the opposite end of the spectrum: the sense of freedom. In moments of confusion, look for the sense of inner peace.

PART 2:
Mind, Ego, and True Self

"The universe tells us a story. We perceive the story. We put it in our language, the birds put it in theirs, and the trees put it in theirs. We can read the story of the universe in the trees. Everything tells the story of the universe....the story has its imprint everywhere....If you do not know the story, in a sense you do not know yourself; you do not know anything."
(Thomas Berry)[5]

Mind, Ego, and True Self

The physical body can be described as a recreation vehicle in which we explore the world. In the same analogy, the mind can be said to be the driver of this recreation vehicle. But what is the mind? There is no physical organ in the brain or anywhere else in the physical body where the mind can be found.

Many spiritual and religious traditions believe that we choose our life circumstances before we are born. We choose the body we have with all its limitations, its positive and negative attributes. Our physical body is a form in which our individual consciousness resides in this particular life. In the same way, it can be said that we choose to have a particular mind. The mind is an energetic entity whose functions are to understand the physical world, to interact with it, and to provide the tools for meaningful contribution and self-realization, i.e. the discovery of the True Self.

What is the True Self? If the mind is the driver, who is the passenger? Who chooses the circumstances of our life? If the body is a vehicle, and the mind is a set of tools, what is our real nature beyond the body and the mind?

Already Happy

There is a well-known fable in Sanskrit poetry and philosophy about the Himalayan musk deer. The stag deer catches wind of the scent of musk and finds it so alluring that he roams the forest and the mountains in pursuit of its source. He exhausts himself in a fruitless search, never realizing the bitter irony: the sweet fragrance he has been chasing resides within himself.

Our own happiness and inner peace are like the scent of the fragrance. We search for them all our lives in the outside world: pursuing possessions, positions, mental and sensual thrills, and superficial relationships. Yet all of these external rewards leave us feeling empty and more lost.

Real happiness and inner peace continue to be elusive. The real reward lies within, where it has always been.

If we could just pause and notice if we are running around, or being mentally busy, in search of something to feel happy about and at peace, we could turn our focus to what is already within us. The happiness and inner peace are already there, in this moment. They are our true nature.

What Stands in the Way

Many spiritual teachers say that inner peace is our true nature. If it is true, then why don't we always feel it? What disturbs our inner peace?

The mind. As human beings, we have a peculiar predicament of pretending we have lost our inner peace. The mind is the instrument that serves this purpose. The mind, always moving, thinking, tossed around with thoughts, desires, expectations, likes and dislikes, distracts us from being at peace. It can be compared to a veil that hangs thick and prevents us from seeing our true nature.

The process of yoga is thinning the veil so we can see. The mind can also be compared to a lake. If the lake is calm, it reflects the moon perfectly. If the lake is rippled, the image of oneself is distorted. Another metaphor for the mind is a mirror that needs to be cleaned to offer a clear reflection.

That is what yoga practice is about. Purification of the mind: *thinning the veil, calming the lake,* and *cleaning the mirror.* The breath and the body are always in the present moment and serve as tools to start your practice.

Greatest Enemy

Much has been said about the ego, a necessary part of the mind. Ancient yogis and modern psychoanalysts alike blame the ego for our woes. What is it? According to yogis, the ego is an illusion of the mind. In Sanskrit, it is called *Ahamkara*.

Once a student approached a famous teacher with a question.

"Master, I try to meditate but my mind is too active. I am not able to pacify it."

"Bring out the mind before me, and I'll pacify it," the Master replied. *"Well, that's the problem, when I look for my mind, I cannot find it."*

"There!" the Master stated, *"it's pacified."*

What this example shows is when we turn our full attention to the mind and look for it, it is not a concrete thing, or a sensation. One moment it's here, the next moment, it's elsewhere. The ego is the same way. Not found in any specific place in the brain, or anywhere for that matter. Yet, it sure does exist. As an illusion. *Ahamkara* has very specific functions. It creates the sense of separateness, the sense of our unique individual self, localized in this body and mind.

The ego compares, competes, trouble-shoots, self-preserves, but most of all it forms a powerful bond of identification with the mind. That means that it makes us believe that we are the mind - so fully and completely that we do not question it unless we experience an awakening.

The ego is *"like a radar on a ship,"* spiritual philosopher Alan Watts[6] used to say. The radar scans its environment and searches for danger. It is a trouble-shooter. If we identify with the trouble-shooter, we define ourselves as being always in trouble. And everyone wonders why they always feel stressed.

Sri Shankara, an eighth-century poet and yogi, called the ego *"the greatest enemy, and the main barrier to Self-Realization."*

As we progress on the spiritual path and learn about the ego and the mind, the ego persists in creating more and more subtle ways to entrap and entangle us in its identification.

Have you experienced an inner calm during a meditation? Only to hear the inner voice saying: *"Wow, I am getting better at this meditation thing!"*

Next thing you know, you walk around feeling a little elated, feeling a little more 'enlightened' than before. Alas, it is still the ego's game. Many teachers, self-proclaimed gurus, and aspirants fall prey to these subtle games.

The only way to know if the ego is not involved is to have silence, a thoughtless and wordless experience, that contains no "I, me, or mine." Sounds simple enough. Yet, according to the Vedas (ancient texts from India), calming the mind and the ego is *"the most difficult task in the entire Universe."*

Game of All Games

What is the most basic of all games? Pretending. We pretend when we play a game. Peek-a-boo or hide-and-seek are basic games that even a baby can understand if you peek at them over a book. We hide something. We conceal something as in a game of cards, or the game of chess where we conceal our strategies. We pretend we do not know or that we cannot see. The goal of the game is to find, to reveal, to discover, to break open the defenses to see what lies within, the prize.

The world is such a game. Life is such a game. In yogic philosophy, this game is known as *Maya*, the illusion that this world is real.

We pretend not to be enlightened. We – meaning Universal Consciousness. We choose our perfect cover – the mind with the function of the ego which powerfully convinces us to identify with it.

The rest of our life, we play peek-a-boo with our True Self. The ego is working hard to prevent us from discovering our True Self. The ego pulls us into ego-identification: We believe we are the mind.

The ego gets stronger as it builds its powerful bonds, and its strategies (to retain its reign) become more subtle as we try to learn about it and its role. It traps us in its self-centered egocentric universe.

But after all, it is still a game. The ego is part of *Maya*, an illusion, a function needed only to play this game of life. It's not real. We are only pretending. After all, we are enlightened: each one of us is part of the all-pervading Universal Consciousness expressed in our own unique way in this life.

The well-known 20th century spiritual teacher, Alan Watts, compared this game to a dream: Imagine if we could dream any dream on purpose, and in any given night, dream up ninety-five years of life, choose the kind of people we would have for our parents, the kind of people we would meet in this dream, who we would spend this dream-life with, and choose all sorts of challenges. When we would wake up from this dream, we would learn a few things, and the next night, we would set up another dream composed of other challenges and situations. After many such nights, after hundreds and hundreds of such dreams filled with every possible pleasure, adventure, and obstacle, we would say: *What if I go to sleep without planning my dream? What if I choose not to plan or to remember my plan, and just dream up a life moment to moment without knowing it ahead of time?* ... And that is the dream-life you are living right now, as you are reading these words. When you wake up (you as Consciousness), you will look back at this life, and learn a few lessons, too.

We are all playing this game of pretending. We are all Consciousness. We are all dreaming this life locked in a human body, and we use the mind to prevent our Selves from seeing the True Self. Why? What is the point?

Imagine if everyone was fully enlightened already, and if all of us were in Pure Bliss all the time. Is there any fun in that? It is after all a lot more fun to play a game. To experience Bliss, one must first experience non-Bliss.

Reflect the Moon

"There are two ways of spreading the Light:
to be the candle or the mirror that reflects it."
– Edith Wharton, American novelist

As mentioned earlier, our mind is much like a mirror. It reflects the Light of the True Self. Our mind is also like a pond that reflects the Moon at night. The calmer the pond, the clearer the reflection.

When we see the Moon's reflection in the pond, we recognize that it is not the Moon, but only its reflection.

Likewise, we can perceive our True Self through the mind only when the mind is perfectly still. However, to see the actual moon, we have to look away from the pond and look up. To know the Self, we must look beyond the mind.

Our True Self is the candle that shines as bright as ten thousand suns. Our serene mind is the mirror that reflects this Light.

Two Wolves of the Mind

A Cherokee elder told stories to his grandchildren as they sat around a fire. The stories were about animals, forests, mountains, warriors, and bravery. At the end of the evening, he finished his tales by saying:

"A fight is going on inside of me. It is a terrible fight, and it is between two wolves. One wolf represents fear, anger, envy, sorrow, regret, greed, arrogance, self-pity, guilt, resentment, lies, and pride. The other wolf stands for joy, peace, love, hope, sharing, serenity, humility, kindness, benevolence, friendship, empathy, generosity, truth, compassion, and faith. … It is a terrible fight…" He paused for a long time, lost in thought.

The children looked at their grandfather expectantly waiting to hear the rest of it. Finally, one of them could not wait anymore: "Which wolf is going to win?" The old Cherokee looked them all in the eye and stated: "The one I feed."

Our minds are composed of what we receive through our senses, known as *Manas* in Sanskrit. What we see, hear, touch, smell, and taste feeds our mind. Our mind is fed by the senses since the time we are born. If the mind is exposed (willingly or unwillingly) to aggression, competition, violence, and negativity, it becomes that. If it is love, peace, compassion, acceptance, and hope, it becomes that. What happens when we identify with our mind? What happens when you think that your mind is who you are?

We are able to mold our minds, and therefore the way that we appear to the world, by making choices to feed our mind positive sensory impressions. This is yoga for the senses. We can control what the *Manas* allow to come in. Begin today – become aware of what kind of sensory input you allow to come in. This includes everything: movies, TV, Internet, books, magazines, phone conversations, people you spend time with, and places you visit.

Because you are here, reading these words, you made a conscious decision to expose your senses to positive impressions, to feed the wolf that represents Love and Healing. Let's continue along this healing path.

Make a mental note to ask yourself before you watch a movie, read a book, talk on the phone, or even take a yoga class: *Will this make my mind more peaceful, more focused, or more agitated and depressed?*

Poisoned Well

This is a well-known fable that similarly highlights the *Manas* (sensory impressions) and the nature of the mind. I have not found the original source of this story although other spiritual teachers like Paolo Coelho[7] and Dan Millman[8] mention it in their writings.

There once was a king who ruled over a vast kingdom. He had many virtues and was loved for his wisdom. People praised and celebrated their king. In the heart of the kingdom, there was a well with pure waters from which all inhabitants drank.

One day, the water well became poisoned. Whoever drank it, became insane. After a few days, since all the people drank the same water, the whole kingdom went crazy. However, as they were crazy together, no one noticed. Except the king. He had a personal water supply leading to his palace which remained pure.

The king knew that something terrible had happened. The people noticed that all of a sudden the king was different. They stopped liking him and seeing him as a good king. He didn't know what to do. He continued drinking his pure water and people have already devised a plan to overthrow him.

The king decided to do something about it. He went into the town and drank some water from the local well. Soon, he became like everyone else. He lost his sanity. Now the people saw that the king was like them again and accepted him.

Typically, the story ends here, demonstrating our need for conformity and the challenge of standing up to the crowd. However, I don't particularly like this ending. Below is the yogic continuation of the story.

Before drinking the water, the king wrote a note to himself. It said: "Drink only the purified palace water."

He gathered some town folk and led them back into his palace, and they all drank the pure water, and one by one regained their sanity.

What does this fable mean? The king is the mind. The water supply is what we feed it through the senses (*Manas*).

If the senses receive healing information (pure water), the king (the mind) is pure. If the senses are exposed to impure intake (violence, aggression, competition), the mind becomes impure, too.

This story shows us that we need to use discernment in our lives and be selective in what goes into our head. This function of discerning intellect is known as the *Buddhi* in Sanskrit.

The *Buddhi* is the higher function of the mind, the discriminative intelligence. It is the *Buddhi* that reflects the Light of the True Self. The *Buddhi* decides to take on yoga, meditation, and other spiritual practices. The Buddhi decides to become a peaceful warrior, and the Earth Guardian.

In scientific terms, the Buddhi can be said to reside in the pre-frontal cortex of the brain, the neo-cortex, and be responsible for our self-awareness. This function of the mind gives us the ability to analyze our own actions, make educated decisions about right and wrong, and self-reflect.

Because of the Buddhi, the neo-cortex of the brain, we can think about our thoughts and feelings, and be the witness of our own mind. In essence, it is the Buddhi that allows us to train the mind to still itself so we can experience our own True Nature which is Pure Consciousness.

Ego:
Do You Really Need to Win?

Some battles are just not worth fighting. Those mundane altercations many people engage in are driven by our sense of individual self, the ego. The ego needs to win every argument. That is how it strengthens itself.

In our core, however, there is no argument. Our True Self does not care if it wins. To the True Self, the concept of winning is absurd. The perspective of the True Self is that of Oneness. The ego sees all of us as separate. To the Self, we are all one and the same. How can there be an argument?

But in the hectic course of the day, our mind 'forgets' this inner Oneness and the ego rules. Dale Carnegie once said: *"The only way to win an argument is not to have one."*

When faced with a conflict, it's good to ask ourselves: *"Do I really need to win? Is it the ego that needs to win?"*

Better for the Ego

It's better not to be the absolute best at anything. When you are the best at something, you cannot marvel at it anymore. You cannot wonder: How in the world do those athletes do it? How could she or he possibly create this kind of art? How could she or he achieve this much? Earn this much?

In fact, you would feel a little guilty to marvel at your own accomplishments. It would be sort of conceited and just plain impolite to do so in public: *"Yeah, that's my painting right there! Great, isn't it?"* Or: *"Yep, I run a 4-minute mile. What can I say, I am fast!"*

Not only would people feel a little envious and say *"Wow, is she full of herself, or what!"* but they would also not marvel at your accomplishment anymore.

Despite this fact, when you hear that it's better not to be the best at anything, automatically your ego reacts *"Well, I'm not so sure about that, I think it's great to be the best at SOMEthing."* That's ego-talk. Just recognize it and let it go.

This does not mean that you cannot be great at something. You can become an accomplished artist or athlete or businessperson, and still sit back and enjoy marveling at other great ones. Marveling at others' success is great for the ego.

When one is the best at something, one should still have the attitude that there is room for improvement. As the Buddhist proverb states: *"Everything is perfect. With much room for improvement."*

Mind is Like Music:
Experience the Pause

Music is not continuous. Among the tones and sounds of music, there is a lot of silence. There would not be a beat if it was not followed by a pause.

Similarly, there would not be Light if there was no darkness to illuminate.

Our mind is like music. It is also not continuous, although it often seems that it never stops working. But in reality, the mind has many bleeps and pauses.

What is a bleep in the mind?

The state of Pure Being. The state in which we can experience the True Self, our individual vibration of the Universal Consciousness within.

When you first begin to meditate, you discover the ever-working controlling nature of the mind. But then, with a little bit of patience, the quiet moments beyond the mind become more and more apparent. With more steady practice, our inner witness learns to identify and rest our attention within those mental pauses to experience the Inner Peace.

Mystery and Magic:
Enjoy the Mystery

The world is full of mystery and magic. How does that make you feel? It's a good feeling, isn't it? Kind of fun. Exciting.

Yet, at the same time, the human mind wants to solve all mystery. We all want to know things, to understand everything. So there is a conflict. We want the mystery to be there, and at the same time, we want to solve it. If we did solve all mystery and there was no more magic, wouldn't that be a little sad? Not fun anymore. What can we do about this conflict?

Is it possible for the mind to solve all mystery? No. Why not? Because the mind is limited. It only sees a tiny fraction of reality. It uses the five senses to understand and gather information. A dog can smell many more smells than we can. An owl or a bat can hear so many more sounds than people. Even a bee can see many more colors than us. What we know is limited. How could we ever know reality through the mind? It is simply impossible.

We are part of the mystery that we cannot grasp with the mind. Yet, we are able to understand it through other means – direct experience.

However, initially, before we dive into the direct experience of the mystical, we need to become aware of it. We need to develop a true sense of wonder of the mystery that we call our body. How does our body know how to breathe? We never taught it. Any activity in our bodies – heartbeat, digestion, circulation - we don't do anything to make them happen. Do we instruct these processes how to function and do we moment-to-moment consciously maintain their functioning? Definitely not.

Isn't that amazing? You are a mystery, even to your own mind. In a yoga class, we get to explore this mystery, we get to notice it, and to wonder at it.

Yogis develop a lot of conscious control over the body, breath, and mind. But for now, we can say: *"It's OK, I like mystery, let me just watch it, marvel at it, I don't need to know everything, there's an Infinite Knowing inside of me."*

Human and Spiritual

Yoga wisdom has many lessons. One important lesson is recognizing that we are both human and spiritual in nature.

On the human side, we are goofy, awkward, and self-involved. On the spiritual side, we are compassionate, loving, accepting, and forgiving. It seems that both are necessary, and identifying with only one could bring problems.

One morning, I was sitting on the lawn, practicing meditation. On that particular morning, I was able to calm my mind and senses, and access a very quiet place inside. At the same time, there was a part of my mind that remained on the surface and carried on the following monologue: *'Wow, I am really good at this. I THINK I am totally getting it. This is it. This is my true nature, being one with everything and nothing. I could feel that I am being part of everything around me. I am so focused right now..'*

This is the ego gratification game. The better you get at meditation, the more subtle the game of the ego is. It went on just a little longer, when I caught myself. THINK was the give-away. There is no THINK in meditation. Despite it, I continued with my practice.

All of a sudden, I heard a loud buzzing sound. I opened my eyes: a giant bumblebee was flying directly at my face. There was no time to THINK. Lightning fast, I fell back on my hands, my face scrunched up, my lips pursed and ready to blow air at the bee. It flew over me. I sat back up and made my legs more comfortable in the cross-legged position, and then, my little scene rolled through my mind. I started to laugh and shook my head at my own awkwardness and humanness. I thought to myself: *'I guess I am not one with my environment if I am still afraid of the bee.'* Nevertheless, I felt very calm and peaceful.

A yoga class is like that. There are moments when we feel awkward, our bodies feel stuck, and our minds feel angry, embarrassed, and judgmental. And there are times in the class, when your body feels at ease and graceful, when your heart is blown open with joy and inner freedom, when you feel compassion and connection to everyone and everything, and when there is such peace inside that your breath stops. Both human and spiritual natures are there.

Lotus Flower and the Shadow

"*A lotus flower blooms out of the mud,*" spiritual wisdom states. Being human with the ego-possessed mind, we've all experienced the "mud", or the deep dark side of the mind.

Often, this dark side of our being is referred to as the Shadow. The concept of the Shadow is not uncommon in yoga, spiritual traditions, and modern psychotherapy. Sigmund Freud, Carl Yung, Joseph Campbell, and many other psychologists and mythologists have explored and written widely about the Shadow.

The Shadow is our ego self, the most selfish part of our mind, and our most delicate self. It has been conditioned by our upbringing, our fears, our failures, our deepest unfulfilled desires, and the most painful experiences. We rarely show it to others or even admit it to ourselves.

In Jungian[9] psychology, the Shadow refers to the unconscious aspect of the personality which our conscious mind does not identify in itself. Our ego rejects or prefers to remain ignorant of the least desirable aspect of our personality. For that reason the Shadow is largely negative.

"*Everyone carries a shadow,*" Jung wrote, "*and the less it is embodied in the individual's conscious life, the darker and denser it is.*" It may be (in part) one's link to more primitive animal instincts, which are superseded during early childhood by the conscious mind (the *Buddhi*).

Yet, the Shadow plays a vital role in our creativity and ultimately in Self-Realization. Without it, there is no growth, no desire to be free. There is no yearning for freedom without the knowledge of bondage. The lotus flower does bloom in muddy ponds.

Imagine what a skillful actor can do when they are in touch with their Shadow. What full and realistic characters they would be able to create!

Or take a musician who writes heart-stirring music. Their Shadow aspect helps the artist access a deep place within that many people can identify with even though they may not admit it to themselves.

Or take a spiritual leader. How much of their Shadow hangs over their Light? Many gurus have a dark Shadow following them with multiple stories of abuse of their power. Others may bring their Shadow into the foreground like the renowned Buddhist teacher Chögyam Trungpa, whose controversial behavior of heavy drinking and partying left many of his students angry and unnerved.

Is there a single individual without a Shadow? I have never met one. Since we all have a dark side, a highly functioning and overly controlling ego, our goal, as fully conscious human beings, should be to bring our Shadow to our awareness, observe its effects on our actions and thoughts, and learn from it. This is how we are able to gain control of our darker tendencies.

What inspiration or motivation can we draw from our Shadow? Can we create art? Are you creating something right now that can be inspired, or fueled by the Shadow?

Getting to know your Shadow may unleash a lot of energy and emotion. Can you channel this energy into your life's work, or art, or service, or athleticism?

Infinite Intelligence

There is a big spider outside our front door. She builds her web every night, and sometimes we watch how she does it. It's the most incredible thing. She works very quickly and deliberately. Her design is flawless and beautiful every time.

How does she know how to do that? Nobody ever taught her. How do all animals know how to do what they do? There is Infinite Intelligence behind all things. No matter how small. Infinite Consciousness is not limited to physical matter, so size does not matter.

The spider knows without knowing. How do we know how to digest our food, or to beat our hearts, or to work our nervous systems? We do not do any of that consciously. Yet, we do it, all at once. That is the true meaning of Omnipotence.

We do not consciously maintain our existence. Yet, we exist. Is there a Force in the Universe that does maintain your being here? You bet there is.

We do not know how exactly we perform the myriad of processes in our body. Yet, it is the Knowing that we all possess. This Knowing is beyond the mind. It is in every cell of our body. We are inseparable from the Intelligence that is behind all things. We are that Intelligence. We are that spider.

Yoga teaches us how to access it, how to feel that we are It. All we need to do is to steady our minds and be.

Take a breath ...

Notice your thoughts ...

Notice the stillness between the thoughts ...

Notice the Energy and Intelligence that constitute you.

One Sunday afternoon, I was standing outside of our house. It was a beautiful summer day. Two butterflies sat on a flowering bush right next to the house. One of them was giant, yellow and black. It may have been a swallowtail. The other one was much smaller, all orange.

All of a sudden, the big one took off. It flew up and, out of nowhere, another butterfly, just like that one, appeared right next to it. They hit into each other, and swirled around in a spiral, hitting their wings against each other. It looked as though they were playing or fighting or mating.

But how did they know to find each other? How did they sense each other and know that they were the same kind of butterfly? They were drawn to each other immediately. There were so many other butterflies, bugs, and birds flying around, but these two attracted each other like a magnet right away.

Just like a spider knows how to spin an intricate design for its web, this too shows that there's an innate Infinite Intelligence behind all things.

Meditation, Samadhi, and True Self

Many people confuse meditation with concentration. Both are yogic practices. Both are important.

When we first sit down to meditate, we practice concentration, *Dharana*. It's a practice of focusing the mind. Most of the time during this process our mind is actually distracted. We make a continuous effort to keep it focused, but it's natural for the mind to drift away.

Ideally we should stick with one concentration technique. "If you are drilling for water it's best to dig deep in one spot rather than dig multiple shallow wells," the common wisdom states.

Concentrating the mind is a habit. This process forms neurological pathways which become easier and more fluid the more we repeat the same technique. After practicing for a long time, for many months or years, concentration on a specific object becomes effortless. Our mind just goes there.

That is what athletes and artists experience when they work on the same technique for many years. Have you ever watched a world-famous musician play? They become one with their music. The pianist, or the violinist, becomes absorbed into his art. Have you watched an elite athlete practice their sport? They get in 'the zone' and are spellbinding to watch because they are so spellbound themselves.

When our concentration becomes perfect, we experience meditation, called *Dhyana* in Sanskrit. Meditation is perfect

Concentration. Meditation is effortless focus on a single point of mental contact. Unlike the process of concentrating, there are no distractions in meditation. In fact, there isn't even the awareness of distractions. The mind is still and resting on a single focal point.

What happens when the mind detaches from that single focal point?

It can go two ways: back to the distracted state or ... to nothing, meaning the mind pauses and does not produce any one thought. This experience is known as Pure Awareness, or the True Self Realization, or *Samadhi* (absorption in True Self).

Samadhi is a non-mental experience. It's outside, or beyond, the mind, inexplicable and unthinkable. This experience is the goal of Yoga.

Here's the paradox: Since *Samadhi* is our True Self, we always have it, and we do not need to search for it, yet somehow it eludes us.

The reason for that is because we identify with the mind too much. When I say "we" – I mean "we the mind." *Samadhi* and the mind are poles apart.

Surprisingly, and ironically for the mind, we go into the *Samadhi* state multiple times each day. We just don't know we do it, because the mind is not able to explain it. The mind picks up where it left off, and the bleep in the mind is ignored.

The trick is to fall into *Samadhi* on purpose, much like we fall asleep. We are not able to say to ourselves exactly at what point in time we fall asleep. It happens because we prepare for sleep: the bedroom is dark and quiet, the bed is comfortable, we feel tired, etc. We prepare for *Samadhi* much the same way: we pick a place with few distractions, we prepare our physical body to be comfortable so it does not distract us with aches and indigestion, and we condition our mind to be still and rest on a single focal point. Then it happens.

All three states are natural and we experience them all day:
• Distracted mind
• Focused mind (meditation)
• *Samadhi* (no mind)

Yoga practice conditions the distracted mind to become a tool for easy entry into Samadhi as well as a tool of selfless service.

True Self resides in the *Samadhi* state. It shines and illuminates like an internal flame. It enlightens our understanding, not from an external source but from within. Once we have this understanding that we are not the mind, that we are That which is greater than any physical form, whether we call it Pure Awareness or Universal Consciousness, True Self, or *Atman* (our individual divine spark), we gain the lasting certainty of inner peace and happiness.

We develop ways to access True Self, the sense of Pure Awareness, throughout the day. We start feeling its presence all the time, which is simply recognizing our true essence that has been there all along. The *Atman* turns into a steady flame and takes the role of our inner teacher.

Nothing could disturb our inner peace then – a smile, or a frown, a word of praise, or scornful criticism. Firmly grounded in True Self, we become invincible to external ups and downs.

Death:
Return to the Ocean of Bliss

Death is a portal into the Superconscious realm - the place we came from before birth. After death, we shed our bodies, and return home - our individual soul (*Atman*) melts into the Consciousness and Intelligence that comprises the Universe, like a wave blending into the ocean.

Death is also a junction at which one can make a leap spiritually. But to die with a peaceful thought, with an enlightened thought, one must cultivate it now.

When I was six or seven years old, I thought about death. It was a summer day and I remember it vividly. We lived in a nine-story apartment building which was part of a complex of four other similar buildings, all forming a giant rectangular courtyard inside.

It was after dinner, around eight o'clock, still very light outside, and my friend and I were walking back toward our apartment building from a park nearby. Then, all of a sudden, we saw a man falling from the sky, from one of the buildings. He was screaming as he fell. That was why we saw him. We heard him first. Then he hit the ground. It sounded like a splash. We ran over to see. A small crowd of passers-by already gathered around him. His skull was split open into pieces. The brain was visible and blood was everywhere. People gasped and shook their heads and held their mouths.

We stood and stared. In a few minutes, somebody put a blanket over him and the ambulances arrived to take the body away.

We went home after that without speaking about it to each other. I went to bed and could not get the images out of my seven-year-old mind. I didn't tell my parents about it either. I remember lying in my bed at night, wide awake, thinking about death, and about that man whose life ended so quickly in front of us. I realized that people die, as obvious as it may sound, but it was a concept I had not thought about before, that death is imminent, that all people die one way or another, and that I too will die one day. It scared me. I lied in my bed and tried not to cry. I kept thinking if there was a way around it, but of course my only consolation was that I was still young and I forced myself to think that I still had a long life ahead of me, that I should not worry, but the fear of death became real and palpable to me from that point on.

A few weeks later, there was a funeral in our neighborhood. In Russia, funerals start at the place of residence of the deceased. The casket is carried out with a solemn procession, somber trumpet music, and a small crowd of family, friends, and community members. On this day, it was the body of a man who was a father to one of the neighborhood kids. We didn't know why he died. We just hang around outside and watched the procession. The son was there. He was around the same age as I was, no more than seven. The boy walked around the small crowd, pointed at the cars waiting to load the casket, and kept saying *"That's my dad who died."* He walked by my friends and I and said the same thing to us. We didn't know how to reply. He smiled when he said it. I don't think he understood what it meant, being that young. I thought to myself, "*I don't think he understands that his father is not going to be coming back.*" Maybe a few days later, the boy finally realized the finality of death. I was sure it would be a deep and painful realization as it was for me.

These examples above are seen from the ego-mind – from our total identification with the physical body as the Self.

If we identify our selves as this body only, then we die as the body dies. The mind dies too, because it's an entity connected to the body. That is why the mind is afraid of death: it knows it will perish. Additionally, the mind does not comprehend death. It has no knowledge of what was before birth and what lies after death. And it has no way of knowing the before and after. The mind can only guess. It can come up with all kinds of possible scenarios of what happens after death.

However, the sense of mind-less existence (as the after-death existence would be) is easily achieved now. In this life. The mind stops in the states of meditation and Samadhi. Those states are similar to the after-death state.

Even without any conscious efforts to meditate and still the mind, our mind pauses throughout the day, and the Atman, our own spark of the eternal undying Consciousness, shines through. It happens many times each day. We feel it, but we do not know it because the mind does not know it. The body feels it, but the mind does not think any thoughts about it because the state of Samadhi is not a mental state and contains no words or thoughts to describe it.

Death can be seen as a type of *Samadhi* experience. It is a return home - back to our original source - wherefrom we venture out into the physical world in a particular body. When we die with an enlightened thought, cultivated throughout our life, our soul, the *Atman*, attains a higher level of Consciousness known as *Maha-Samadhi*. It is commonly said that when an enlightened individual passes, they attain *Maha-Samadhi*. Such individuals join the Superconscious state before the actual death of their body.

I realize that all this talk about death and the Superconscoius and the *Atman* may be too much for some people. The main thing to remember here is that there is no need to be afraid of death as I was when I was young, or as many people are afraid of and demonize death. Death is not a dreadful specter with a scythe. It is a beautiful transition, a return to the Ocean of Bliss.

PART 3:
Practice

"The stories people tell have a way of taking care of them. If stories come to you, care for them. And learn to give them away where they are needed. Sometimes a person needs a story more than food to stay alive. That is why we put these stories in each other's memory. This is how people care for themselves. One day you will be good storytellers. Never forget these obligations."
(B. Lopez)[10]

Practice

As a discipline for the mind, yoga contains numerous paths and principles that may be practiced in countless ways.

The goal of yoga is to experience the state of True Self Realization. For that to occur on a continuous sustainable basis, certain habits need to be in place. These habits predispose our every-day mind to focus and notice the state of Pure Awareness that is indicative of the True Self experience.

A calm and focused mind has to be trained to be that way through practice. Not only does the mind have to develop a great deal of focusing ability at will, but our emotional predisposition must be firmly grounded in virtuous qualities of stress-free equanimity, compassion, non-violence, and self-control.

Various yogic practices condition your mind to be under your conscious control and bring you to lead the life you envision. We manifest what we focus on. Practice makes perfect, but more importantly "practice makes character." The more we practice something, the more we become it.

Practice trains our nervous system to execute desirable actions automatically whether it's the ease and fluidity of our physical body due to years of practicing the same postures or movements, or an automatic response to a stressful situation when we have conditioned ourselves to breathe deeply, or an instant connection to our Inner Self because we have honed the technique of focusing on it over a long period of time so it also becomes automatic.

When I was eight years old, I went to a Judo club. Judo is a Japanese martial art that is very popular in Russia. I did not tell my parents, because going to Judo with my friends after school meant skipping the gymnastics class I was already attending. But Judo was a lot more fun.

My instructor, a kind quiet unassuming man in his early thirties who was a three-time world champion, suggested that I practice and perfect one technique that suited my shorter build: We called it "throw from the knees." This technique involved pushing into your opponent slightly to get them to push back, and as soon as I would feel their push coming my way, I would use the momentum of their in-coming force to throw them over my head by quickly whipping around and dropping down to my knees in front of them, their body somersaulting over my head with their legs up in the air. I had practiced that move so many times on so many different training partners that I could perform it with my eyes closed and without fail. When wrestling in a tournament, it was just a matter of time of catching my opponent off balance and I would execute the technique. Many boys from other schools knew that it was my 'move.' Their coaches would warn them to watch out for it. But despite their warnings, even if I was losing a match, I would inevitably find a moment when my opponent was slightly off balance, and flip them on their back. I only had one technique that worked, but it worked perfectly every time. The reason was my many hours of practice. I think of my Judo instructor every now and then and mentally thank him for being a great role model for many kids in our neighborhood.

Every morning my father had the following routine: dynamic stretches before running outside for three miles, followed by dumping bucketfuls of freezing water over his head, then finishing with yoga asanas at home mixed with Qi Gong exercises. The whole procedure would take him an hour and a half. He got up at five-thirty every morning.

When I turned seven years old, my father started to wake me up at six thirty, and instead of practicing his usual yoga regimen, he would take me outside and run a few laps around a nearby park with me. At first, I hated waking up early, and did not particularly like running. After several weeks, running with my father for a few laps around the park became my regular morning routine. Even in the midst of Siberian winters, we would layer up with two pairs of gloves and two hats, and trudge through the snowed-in paths.

When it came to running at school in the Physical Education classes, all of a sudden I developed into a good runner in my class, eventually being able to outpace older kids too. Running for my school at track meets became part of my identity at school. My nickname used to be "Elektronik" after a popular children's movie titled "Adventures of Elektronik" which was about a synthetic boy created by a crazy but caring scientist. Elektronik looks just like any other ten or eleven year old, so other pupils and teachers in his school do not know he is not human. There is a part in the movie when Elekronik has to run, and he zooms away at an incredible speed - his legs moving so fast, they are a blur. Despite the track sessions at school, I never skipped my morning runs with my father, my 'secret training' that prepared me for the competition at school.

With my father's daily influence, yoga and martial arts were part of my every-day language, and my friends viewed me as a source of knowledge on any Eastern ideas and practices. I managed to inspire a few of my friends to start our own special 'elite ninja yoga' training. We met almost every evening after dinner on top of a hill and practiced stretches, martial arts moves, climbing on and jumping off low-level buildings, and meditation. The meditation was always the finale of the evening. We sat on top of that hill cross-legged, and in silence, listening to our fast-beating hearts after running through the night, and to the sounds of twilight. In the summer, it would not get dark until one o'clock in the morning, although many bright stars would be visible. Our gatherings lasted for several years until we got old enough to be more interested in chasing girls instead, and had more schoolwork in order to graduate in good standing.

No one becomes a yogi without practice. We all have many layers of mental conditioning that allow us to function well in today's world but simultaneously prevent us from experiencing our True Self. That is why practice is needed to clear the clutter, and instill the habitual pathways for Self-Awareness.

What are some of the most common and effective practices in yoga? What habits do yogis instill to predispose their mind for the Nirvana experience? The following are some of my favorite practices and stories that relate to such practices.

How to Create Change in the World

Yoga wisdom tells us that we start at the most basic level. To create change, begin with an individual. What is even more basic than a single human being? The stuff we are all made of: atoms and subatomic particles. "You are what you eat" as the saying goes. But what about our mind? Is the mind also made of atoms? Not exactly…

Physically, we may consist of atoms, but mentally we are made out of stories. To create change, we need to change the stories that our minds are made of.

What is an atom, by the way? An atom is the most basic unit of every living and non-living thing. But isn't that just another story? … Everything is a story.

When you were born, your parents told you the story that they were told by their parents, who, in turn, were told by their own parents. This re-telling has been going on since the very beginning of humankind. Yet, who was the original storyteller?

Our teachers, parents, friends, and peers contribute to that on-going story. They give us the only description of the world they know - their perception of the world. It may not be how the world really is. We ourselves contribute to the story of the world every moment of our existence by thinking and believing in what we have been told.

The stories we tell ourselves form our social and cultural values. This means that our stories, tales, fables, anecdotes, parables, proverbs, and colloquial expressions are the backbone, the building blocks, of our society as a whole, and our modern culture on the planet Earth.

For the last few thousand years, the stories that have dominated our consciousness, in most modern cultures, are the stories of mankind's rule over the natural world, of the sense of separateness from nature and from each other, of the value of independence (instead of inter-dependence) and of our self-gratifying pre-occupation with our ego-mind.

No matter how simple and seemingly insignificant, our stories are the real cause of many global social and cultural problems such as war and violence; fear of the natural world and separation from nature; pollution, environmental destruction, and loss of wildlife habitats; over-consumption, materialism, inequality, and poverty.

Imagine if our stories were teaching us some virtuous value, or encouraging us toward a positive action. I mean all of our stories.

Imagine re-writing these metaphors:

"Kill two birds with one stone" would be *"Feed two birds with one seed."*

"It's a dog-eat-dog world" would be *"It's a happy-dog-splashing-in-the-pool world."*

"Take as much as you can, before someone else does" would become *"Take only what you need, leave the rest for others."*

If our description of the world as we know it was always based on universal love, compassion, and interconnectedness, what would the world be like?

Nonetheless, our world is the way it is for a reason. We've all done our part in creating it. What matters now are the stories we tell. If we want to continue seeing abundance on this beautiful planet, some of our stories have to change.

Although it would take some time and effort, we can focus on making this process a journey filled with fun, exploration, learning, and love.

We need to become more aware of the existing stories and re-tell them in a more positive light. We need to learn from the older cultures that have survived modernization and from their stories, as well as from countless teachers and seekers who have taken this path of wisdom in the past. We must take time to witness life and nature, and notice the innumerable lessons all around us. We must listen closely to our own hearts as they are also our teachers and tell their own unique story.

It is, in fact, very real and possible to create change in the world that is full of love and happiness. It may be our next evolutionary step, to transform to a more spiritual way of living, with stories as the vehicle.

Let's begin today. Create change within you. If your day is beginning, will you keep your eyes and ears open for a positive story? What positive story can you share with others today?

If this is the end of the day, what positive story did you hear today? What moved you today in a positive way? Perhaps, it's worth remembering, writing it down, and sharing it with others.

When I Get Better...

It seems that many people have a tendency to postpone what they really want to do. They typically say "I just need to make sure I do this other thing first, then I can start my yoga practice, or meditation practice, or my journal, or start writing my book, or travel somewhere."

Recently, I was teaching a private yoga therapy session to a regular client of mine when she said *"When I get better at this, I'll start my regular home practice."* As soon as she said it, I realized that she had been saying this same phrase for the last three years.

"Do you know that you have said that to me before?" I said to her with a smile.

"I have?"

"Yes, many times."

"I guess you are right." She agreed. *"So what does it mean?"*

"That it's a habit," I said. *"We habitually tell ourselves the same beliefs and convictions. The truth is 'you are better at this now!' This is the better moment. You don't have to wait to get better."*

Often, we delay experiencing special moments right now because of this habitual tendency.

Sometimes, it may be the fear of the unknown that stops people from doing what they always wanted to do. However, often it's just a habit.

Notice if there is anything in your life that you are delaying. Have you observed yourself uttering a similar phrase? Is it time to change your language patterns and recognize that this moment is actually the best moment?

Now is the time to start. There is no better time than now. This is the perfect moment to begin what you wanted to do all your life.

This practice of accepting everything as already perfect is called *Santosha*, the practice of contentment.

Santosha is being content with who you are in this life, where you live, what you have, and what you do.

We often hear ourselves and other people say "When I move there, I'll be happier" or "When I get that done, I'll be happier" or "When this happens, I'll be in a better place."

What happens when we finally move, or accomplish that thing?

We may feel better for a while, but then we find the next thing to get, or to accomplish. The grass seems to be always greener elsewhere. That is just how the mind works. The mind is never really happy where it is.

Instead, we make it our habit to say: "This moment of my life is actually IT! I am the person now whom I always wanted to be."

Our mind may not agree with it, and may give reasons why it is not true. But to practice *Santosha*, we maintain: "I am exactly where I always wanted to be. It may not seem that way. But this is the perfect moment, I am living the perfect life, full of challenges and adventures perfect for me right now."

Think about that concept for a moment. Have you considered it? That this is actually your best moment.

Years later you may look back at this very moment and say to yourself, "Yeah, that was a good time."

Santosha is a daily habit of recognizing this inherent perfection of who you are, what you do, and where you live, regardless of how hard life may seem.

How to Change Your Life:
Samskara

Imagine you walk down the street on the way to work and see a coffee shop. You decide to stop in and get a latte. It's not something you would normally do but you just feel like it on this day.

In a few days, you pass by the same place, and think to yourself "That was good the other day. I'll get a latte again."

In a few weeks, you find yourself stopping by the same coffee shop almost every day. It has become a habit. After a while, you find it hard not to stop by for your daily latte.

In yoga, we call it a *Samskara*, a deep-seated pattern of behavior or pattern of thinking. Samskaras are like deep impressions or grooves in the mind that cause most of our actions and compel us to do what we do. Often, against our common sense, as with many addictions. Many smokers would like to quit, but they cannot. It's too habitual. We are like trains on a track. We may want to get off, or go a different way, but we cannot change.

We develop *Samskaras* over the course of our lives. Good and bad. Helpful and harmful.

A healthy body and a peaceful mind are the causes of *Samskaras* that nourish them. Just as with an addiction, to create a healthy habit, we must do it over and over again until it's second nature, a deep groove.

A firmly established meditation practice is a *Samskara*. Eating healthy is a *Samskara*. So is any self-disciplining practice. As is our reaction to change, our reaction to stress, how we treat others, and how we approach learning, work, relationships, and love.

It seems simple. All we need to do in order to have a healthy body and a peaceful mind is to commit to creating some positive *Samskaras* in our lives – *Samskaras* that bring love, gratitude, compassion, kindness, cheerfulness, joy, and a sense of meaning.

What type of action can each of us perform each day, for example, to create Love? Once we commit, and stick to it for a few weeks, the mind forms a *Samskara*, and it becomes easier and easier to perform, until it becomes a deeply-engrained habit and takes over our life.

We identify with our *Samskaras*. Typically, when asked "Who are you?" we think of ourselves as a "healthy person," or a "kind person," or an "intense person," or an "adventurous person," or a "smoker," a "fun-loving people person," an "anxious person," and so on.

All of these identity labels have been created in our minds. For example, if we see ourselves as a "kind person," we follow the actions (*Samskaras*) that define a "kind person," thereby reinforcing our behavior and our belief in who we are.

Once aware of your *Samskaras* and your identity, you can begin to make a change to be the person you want to be. Perform a simple action each day that a "kind person" would perform. Soon enough you will be one.

If you are dealing with a harmful *Samskara*, make an effort to take a simple action each day to reverse that harmful habit. If you are a smoker, for example, first instruct your mind to change that identity – tell yourself that "you are not a smoker anymore," and that "you used to be one." Second, practice deep breathing every time you feel the need to reach for a cigarette. Cue yourself to breathe deeply for two full minutes before you decide to smoke or not to smoke. Notice the relaxing and simultaneously energizing effect of the full breath on your body and mind. It will not be easy at first. *Samskaras* are hard to change. But the more often you do it, the deeper the new groove. Soon enough, your self-identity will change, too, without ever going back.

Non-Violence and Selfless Action
Why Kill Two Birds with One Stone...

When you can feed two birds with one seed? Non-violence is a foundational principle of Yoga and its central practice. Yoga teaches us to examine our actions, words, and even thoughts.

When most people come across our common expressions like the 'two-birds' one above, they usually do not notice the insensitivity or violence that may be associated with it. As you integrate yogic principles into your life, you become aware of your every expression, every gesture, and intention – Is it violent? Is it harmful? Or is it peaceful? Does it help others? Everything is seen through the lens of Non-Violence.

Non-violent attitude is the foundation for Inner Peace. If you would like to maintain your peace of mind in any situation, practice *Ahimsa* (Sanskrit for non-violence).

Mahatma Gandhi brought India its independence by making *Ahimsa* his central lifelong practice. He examined his every word and thought. He made his diet vegetarian, and performed all his actions as a selfless service.

That sounds daunting, but Non-Violence is simply a habit. As with any habit, it can be developed and ingrained deeply into your nature. For that, conscious daily awareness is necessary.

Take a moment in the morning of each day to pause for a minute and mentally instruct yourself to be more mindful of your language, thoughts, and actions. "Let me be mindful and peaceful in my actions, words, and thoughts."

Likewise, take another minute at the end of each day, to pause and examine your day and extract any lessons from it:"Did I retain my inner peace in this particular situation? What could I have done differently to stay more mindful and peaceful?"

My One Hunting Trip

In yogic philosophy, there are five principles for social conduct called the *Yamas*. The *Yamas* are the abstinences, i.e. actions and behaviors we are advised to avoid.

Ahimsa is the first of the *Yamas*. The other four are *Satya* (truthfulness), *Asteya* (non-stealing), *Aparigraha* (non-hoarding or moderation), and *Brahmacharya* (faithfulness).

They seem very similar to some religious laws, and certainly echo the Ten Commandments in Christianity. Although it is probably the other way around: the Commandments came later, since the Yoga Sutras were written at least five hundred years prior, and these practices preceded Christian faith by over a thousand years.

The biggest difference, however, is that breaking one of these principles does not result in sinful character, societal shame, and the accompanied sense of guilt. Instead, these are simply guidelines for maintaining our Inner Peace. If you break one of them, you lose your Inner Peace. If you abide by these principles, you retain your peace. It's as simple as that.

No one is perfect. We have all broken a few of these principles in our past. That is what being human with a fully functional ego entails. We make mistakes. But hopefully, we can learn from them.

We try to process our mistakes to extract the lessons. Typically, it is during our quietest moments, during our deepest meditations, that a broken principle surfaces to our awareness and haunts us. If we have been violent, untruthful, greedy, immoderate, and unfaithful at any point in our life, that memory of that experience appears and disturbs our inner peace.

That is why the yogis have always given the precautionary advice to follow the Yamas: to retain our Inner Peace even in our deepest meditations.

Personally, I have a story that disturbs my peace of mind. I believe that I have come to terms with it and let it go, yet it remains a memorable lesson.

When I was about twelve years old, my father took me on a hunting trip. He never went hunting but this time he was invited by a friend and decided to go, bringing me along.

It was late fall, probably mid-December, and the snow covered the pine forests with thick blankets. The temperatures in the day were below − 20 Celsius (about − 25 F), and colder at night. We traveled in our friend's van all day on snow-covered winding bumpy country roads. I remember being very cold on that ride. I sat in the back of the van quietly with a surly grimace questioning our decision to go in the first place.

We arrived at a log cabin lodge as the darkness fell on the forest, around 3pm. Behind the lodge I saw a large fenced-in yard with dog kennels and twenty to thirty Siberian huskies and other hunting dogs huddled together in the center of the yard. A few of them got up and barked at us in greeting, some wagged their tails, and most of them barely moved their eyes to acknowledge us.

The lodge contained several simple rooms with wooden bunk beds built into the walls. In the center, a giant hearth burned with wood-fed fire and warmed the entire house. Glowing embers crackled loudly. I sat in front of it to warm up.

Three or four other men greeted us inside the house. These were professional hunters, I learned later. Working on commission for the Soviet government, they hunted fox, sable, pheasant, deer, and bears. The dogs outside belonged to them.

Within the next couple of hours, more hunters arrived. Most of them knew each other. These were rough men not accustomed to speaking gently or minding their language around children. I am sure my father had to bite his tongue many times during our time at the lodge.

I did not mind. I felt warm and watched the dogs out the window. By five o'clock, we sat down on long wooden benches at a big oak table for early dinner. I cannot remember what we ate. Probably soup with coarse brown bread, which I loved, and some kind of meat: fish or pork, with potatoes. Russians are very predictable about their food choices in the winter.

Altogether there were about eight men. I was the only child. Very quickly after dinner, my father motioned to me in the direction of my bunk bed and encouraged me to go to sleep early. I got the point. As vodka bottles started to empty, the conversations at the dinner table turned more rambunctious and uncensored. I was glad to leave. Yet, I could not sleep. The men were loud and used so much profanity that it sounded like a contest of who can sound more vulgar. They told jokes and stories, about women, about the army (where they all served), and about their hunting life.

The Russian language is exceptionally rich in vulgar expressions and contains thousands of jokes which we call 'anecdotes.' It is a very popular pastime for many Russians to tell anecdotes sitting around the dinner table. Many of these anecdotes distill the essence of Russian culture and, under the guise of metaphors, used to poke fun at the inefficiencies of the Soviet state. Most common jokes were about the Soviet leaders, about dull and corrupt army generals, about the Jews, and the Poles, and the Chukchas (native people of Northern Siberia).

This rich and diverse narrative of self-directed humor has no doubt been born out of the suffering of the people. When no tears are left to cry, people tell jokes. Humor became a way of dealing with the hardships of Russian life since the Tsarist times. Millions of Russians were sent to Gulags (labor camps and concentration camps) during Stalin. The language evolved to reflect the hard life and the prison-like culture of the exiles.

As I lied there on my bunk bed, warm and fed, I was thoroughly inundated with the richest and most vivid examples of this slice of Russian culture. Their voices boomed with laughter as each of them took a turn at the next joke. I recognized the clear voice of my father as he too joined the go-round. He was a colonel in the army and, using his natural gift of charisma and love for all things theatrical, commanded attention and easily bonded with this unlikely crew.

Cigarette smoke hung in the air in thick layers. I remember covering my nose and mouth with my blanket to breathe and feeling nauseous. The dogs outside howled. Or maybe it was the wind howling. Slowly the banter around the table quieted and turned to their hunting stories.

I remember one story told by a hunter with the dogs. He came upon a bear's tracks in the snow and his dogs took off to chase it. He readied his rifle and sprinted after the dogs. He knew he had to run as hard as he could. The dogs, as tough as they are, were no match for a brown bear. If he did not get there soon, he would lose all of them. As he cleared the final cluster of trees, he witnessed the following scene. A giant bear sitting back on its haunches swatted at the lunging dogs as if they were flies. Out of his eight dogs, six dogs lay motionless on the ground, some decapitated, others with their final gasping breaths.

The remaining two dogs circled the bear cautious to attack. The hunter cocked his rifle and fired several shots. The bear's body shuddered and rocked back onto its front feet. The dogs ripped into its throat causing little damage. The hunter ran closer and unloaded several more shots, killing the animal. He concluded his story by repeating that a single sweep of a bear's paw can decapitate a dog, and then, proudly, that he still had the fur coat of that bear.

I remember feeling bad for the bear and for the dogs. I remember I could not decide which of the animals were 'bad' and why they had to die and suffer so much. Then I fell asleep.

We woke up to a crisp morning with bright-blue sky and a moderate negative 15 degrees. Most hunters were already gone. There were no dogs left in the yard. My father and I sat down for bread-and-eggs breakfast with our friend and another man who seemed very friendly. They discussed our plan. We were supposed to look for wild hares and pheasant.

The snow was powder and barely crunched under our feet as we headed out single-file down a narrow snowy trail. I was given a small rifle called a Karabiner which was made of laminated dark oak and black steel and, after a few minutes, started to weigh heavy on my shoulder.

Once deep in the woods, we stopped every few steps to listen and look around. Finally, the hunter friend spotted a wild hare and pointed in its direction. The light-grey hare sat on alert among a couple of young pines. The hunter motioned me to come over. *"Do you see it?"* he whispered. I nodded. *"Do you want to take a shot at it?"* I looked over at my father. He nodded sternly. *"Sure,"* I said. The hunter set the Karabiner into the front of my shoulder. *"Shoot!"* he whispered as I hesitated. I lined up the sight lines with my target and pulled the stiff trigger. The sound of the shot hurt our ears and bounced off the tall pines ringing like a church bell. Then, we heard another sound. This new sound I will never forget. It was a scream of the hare, sharp, high-pitched and human-like. The hunter shouted: *"You hit him, but the bullet just braised him."* The hare was gone. I stood breathless and confused. The hunter hopped over the deep snow toward the spot. He looked around and shook his head *"It's gone!"*

"What was that?" I mumbled, finally.

"The hare scream when they are injured." The hunter replied. *"That was the hare?"* My voice trembled. I didn't want to believe it. I could feel tears welling up in my eyes. My father looked over at me and understood what was going through my head.

"You don't have to shoot if you don't want to." He whispered.

The men exchanged glances and silently continued on the narrow path.

Since that day, that moment, I made myself a promise that I would never shoot at a living creature again. That cry of the hare haunts me to this day. This memory comes back to me even in my most peaceful moments.

Of Monks and Birds

In Thailand, there are hundreds of temples and even more monks. Thousands of them in any major city. Wherever you go, you always see them, in their orange robes, with their solemn and peaceful attitude, steady and purposeful manner of walking and dealing with the world.

I noticed that every time I saw a monk, I felt an instant message of non-violence and peace. Just by being who they are, they send that message, knowingly or not, consciously or not.

Thai people love and support the monks. So I am sure that most people feel the same subconscious vibration of non-violence and peace when they see a monk. They are lucky in Thailand, because they get this vibration many times a day. This creates a very peaceful atmosphere. Even in Bangkok, overpopulated and polluted, you get influenced by the constant positive presence of numerous temples and monks.

After I noticed this, I made a point to watch other people on the street when they saw monks. I watched people pause for a split second recognizing something spiritual within themselves as well, I saw their faces becoming more relaxed, their eyes more kind, their actions more considerate. Wow, I thought, so simple and yet so powerful.

I wondered about what we can do in the United States, and other countries, to get the same effect. And then I remembered the story of an ivory woodpecker that symbolized wilderness and became extinct. This fact upset people. Everyone was saying that there's no more wilderness left. Then, not too long ago, this same woodpecker was spotted in Arkansas. It was back!!! Wow, this sent a huge wave of joy through the whole bird-watching and nature-loving community. One sighting of a bird created this powerful ripple.

Why not use any and every bird, or even any form of life that you happen to see in your day, as a symbol of peace and non-violence? Just like the monks, we can use birds and other animals. Any time you see one, pause, take a breath, notice where you are, and recognize that they are part of your reality and maybe you are here to help them with a kind and peaceful thought.

Mirrors

Namaste or Namaskar is a common greeting in India. Namaste translates as "I recognize my divine nature because I see it shine in you," or simply "I see my Self in you." It reflects the recognition of our deep connection to each other as different manifestations of the same Universal Consciousness. We are all part of the same One Consciousness.

In effect, we are all mirrors to each other. When you look at others, you see your own reflection, the reflection of humanity in all of its forms.

When you meet someone, you can see the spark in their eyes, and a spark of their spirit. You can recognize the same tendency of their mind to wander and to focus and then to wander again. You can tell by looking at them that they are, too, in a similar predicament as you are - pulled in multiple directions between human responsibilities and living a spiritual life, getting caught up in the ego-mind and hearing the subtle whispers of the inner heart.

When you catch eyes with someone next time, remember that they are just as you are. Exchange the sparks in the eyes. Recognize their spiritual nature. Bow your head in recognition and offer a silent salutation of "Namaste."

Social Masks:
The Mask That Makes a Difference

A friend told me that he once had an opportunity to ask an enlightened master a question.

He asked: *What is the best feeling that you've ever had and the worst feeling?*

Master's answer was: *The best feeling is to wake up in the morning with a clear mind. To wake up and be free of any worries or emotional disturbances. To feel total Peace and Joy for the rest of the day, even when you have duties and responsibilities.*

And the worst feeling is to pretend to be enlightened when you know that you are not.

The way I see it is sort of opposite. We are enlightened but we pretend that we are not. Knowing that we are enlightened is not a bad feeling. It's inspiring to know that you are enlightened, isn't it? But pretend to be enlightened and, in the back of your mind, think *"Oh, well, I am really a fake"*, that's not a good feeing. So I agree with that.

We all have a social mask or masks. It is a yogic practice to become aware of your social masks, and make the image you present to the world a useful tool. A tool that is used to help others.

As poet John Masefield once wrote:
"Three men went down the road
As down the road went he:

The man they saw,
The man he was,
And the man he wanted to be."

How can we merge these multiple masks? Answer is simple: Do good for others. We all want to be happy.

The only way to be happy is to grow, evolve, and contribute to others. Helping others makes our life meaningful.

At first, we need to accept ourselves right where we are. What better way to practice such acceptance than in a yoga class? Connecting with the simplicity of our bodies, with the honesty of our bodies, with their limitations, and recognizing how busy our minds are, and how complex. Trying to stay in the moment, listening, accepting, not pretending that we know anything, not pretending that we are somewhat enlightened or spiritual. And then, maybe, as we find ourselves in the moment that is beyond the mind, we may feel Peace and Joy.

If you must wear a mask, as we all do, why not make it a mask that makes you learn and grow, and makes a difference in the lives of others?

Karma:
Yoga of Action

Most of our actions cause some sort of a reaction. This is a natural law of cause and effect. Every action has an equal and opposite reaction. In yoga, and in Hindu philosophy, this is called *Karma*, action and reaction. A friend of mine told me a story about Karma. The story is cute and a little silly, but it illustrates the point.

A young Indian man liked a young Indian woman, and decided to impress her. He held a matchbox with one hand, opened it, took out one match, and, using only one hand, flipped the match against the side of the box so that it would light up. But he forgot to close the box. So the match set fire to the rest of the matches and the whole matchbox went up in flames. It burned his fingers. He flinched in pain. The woman shook her head side to side and said: *"Instant Karma."* So much for impressing her.

Sometimes, *Karma* is instant. Often, however, it takes a long time to receive the repercussions of our actions. Yogis distinguish between three types of *Karma*, and compare it to a bow and arrows.

There is past *Karma* – arrows you have shot from the bow - actions we have caused in the past and are living their effects right now – it is the reason you are alive and find yourself in these particular circumstances; this type of *Karma*

- we cannot do anything about, it's best to accept it and do the best we can.

There is present *Karma* – you are holding an arrow in your bow ready to let go and you have a choice – these are actions you are making at this moment in time and you have control over them.

Finally, there is future *Karma* – all other arrows in the quiver – you cannot do much about them right at this moment.

In Hinduism, *Karma* is a law, like gravity. As you live your life, you accumulate *Karma*. The Hindus call it a bag, or a sack, of *Karma*, that you lug around with you all of your life. *Karma* is responsible for the concept of reincarnation, or returning to the physical body again and again endless number of times.

When you near the end of your life, not all of your *Karma* is lived out, or accounted for. As your body passes, the leftover *Karma* forces your individual soul to return to life to continue living out the leftover *Karma*. It's like a pebble dropped in a pond that creates ripples going out and coming back to the center. The ripples of your actions come back to you, and make your soul return to the physical life.

Karma is created by all actions: good and 'bad.' The cycle of birth and rebirth seems endless. How then does one break out of this cycle?

There is only one way, according to yogis: the path of *Karma* Yoga, the yoga of selfless action.

When we throw a boomerang, it comes back to us. How can we throw it so it does not return? If we throw it to someone else.

Karma is only created if our actions are carried out or directed for our own benefit. If our actions are performed for the sake of others, no *Karma* is accumulated, and we rid ourselves of its bondage.

Yogis dedicate their lives to performing selfless actions. Live for the sake of others. Create no *Karma*.

Swamis, or the Hindu monks, dedicate their lives to this path of selfless action. They renounce their attachments to possessions and to personal benefits. The color of their robes, orange, signifies the color of fire, the flame of purification, that serves to remind them of their resolution for the rest of their lives.

After many years of such practice, their *Karma* is reduced, or completely banished. Then, the path to Enlightenment is open, and the moment of Self-Realization occurs spontaneously. Their lives are free of *Karma* and their minds have been purified through their tireless selfless work.

For everyone else out there, the non-Swamis of the world, we are constantly performing actions that make an impact on ourselves and others. Let's stop to think about which actions are self-centered and which are selfless.

Is buying a new car, shoes, book, (...) selfless? Can it be used to serve others? Is traveling selfish, or can it be used to improve the lives of others? Is attending a school or college, or taking a yoga class, self-centered? Or can it be used to create positive change in the world?

All actions can be seen through the lens of *Karma* Yoga. What about a yoga class? It may seem selfish at first. We are practicing physical postures and deep breathing to have stronger bodies, better health, and more focused minds.

What if we adjust our perspective to make this physical practice less self-centered?

We can cultivate all these benefits for other's sake. We need stronger bodies, better health, and more focused minds to be of better service to our friends, families, and others in need. We can be more available to others when more physical health and mental focus is available to us.

If you are going to take a yoga class, adjust your perspective: make your practice for the sake of others. As you stretch and strengthen, think how you are getting more fit to inspire and help others. Also remember the instant Karma – the immediate effect of the yoga postures. Make sure your practice is not to impress anyone, including yourself, or get injured, but instead it is healing, care, and love.

We may also choose to dedicate our practice to someone else. Next time you take a yoga class, or practice asanas at home, imagine someone you know well who needs to practice yoga but is resistant to start. Imagine them next to you during your whole practice. Their mat next to your mat.

Pause occasionally, especially when you feel a flow of energy, fullness of breath, or an inner stillness. Imagine your friend feels the same sensation. Allow the benefits of your practice and the good energy to flow over to them, to be shared with them.

This practice becomes selfless. You dedicate your practice and its benefits to someone else. If practicing this way becomes a habit, your life becomes a selfless act, free of Karma.

Yoga in Action:
How to Succeed

There is a story about "The Man Who Planted Trees"[11] in the region of Provence in the foothills of the French Alps. The man in the story takes joy in the process of planting trees. He does not have a goal in mind, or any expectations from his actions. He loves the land, even though the land is desolate and arid. He seems to be happy to connect to the land itself. He collects acorns many miles away, brings them to this place, and plants them with great care and love every single day. He walks around making holes in the ground with his curling pole in perfect rows dropping the acorns into the holes. One seed at a time. One step at a time. For many years.

Years later, those oak trees grow into huge forests. Biologists wonder what happened, what caused this transformation in the land. The trees bring moisture, rain, birds, bees, and other life. Over ten thousand people move to the area. The land is transformed entirely. It's a miracle.

Yet, the cause is the work of one man. One single individual, working without expectations, tirelessly, with love.

In yoga, we talk about a practice becoming firmly grounded. This means creating a lifestyle which brings very specific results: health, peace, happiness. However, yogis are deliberate not to mention to expect any results. Once we expect a certain outcome, our minds get in the way: we forget about the love and the care and about being happy about the process.

The yogis provide only three criteria for creating a successful practice (i.e. achieving anything): practice for a long time, on a regular basis, and take your work seriously (love and care).

For a long time – Regularly – With love and care.

That is the recipe for success: to create lasting health and happiness and find peace. Like forests that grow out of tiny seeds, your life and your work depend on your approach. Focus on the action with love and care, forget about the outcome.

Disappearing Ant:
Small Acts of Compassion

One morning, I was practicing yoga outside as usual and going through my routine, which varies once in a while, but I always keep a few favorite yoga poses.

I was in Downward-Facing Dog when I saw a black ant crawling right in the middle of my mat. I thought to myself 'Poor Ant' and kept going through my routine. Then in a few moments, I was in Down Dog again, looking down, and there it was – that ant. Now I thought 'Maybe I should help the ant'. But I really don't like to interrupt my flow, even for something important. And then a thought came:

'I don't have to interrupt my flow – picking up that ant and saving its life is just another yoga pose – it is part of the flow.'

In fact, everything always is and should be considered part of the flow. Very mindfully, still breathing and aligned, I paused, gently took the ant between my fingers, and was about to set it on the grass. Out of nowhere, a gust of wind came and lifted the front edge of my mat. I looked down and realized that suddenly the mat was hovering above the ground! Levitating! ... No, just kidding. But I got your attention! I was about to set the ant on the ground, but the ant was gone. I looked everywhere, on my hand, on the mat, in the grass, and it was nowhere to be found.

I thought the wind must have taken it. Or maybe, the Universe wanted to teach me a lesson: to take the time to perform an act of compassion no matter how small, even if it 'interrupts my flow,' and to include every compassionate act into the flow.

Bodhisattva

A Bodhisattva is an enlightened individual who attained enlightenment in a past life, and, instead of remaining in a more subtle plane of existence, being one with the Universal Consciousness, they choose to come back to this physical world in a physical body.

Imagine a beautiful fruit garden with the most delicious fruits. Imagine being so hungry for those fruits. But there is a very tall wall enclosing the entire garden. You try to climb it, to jump to reach its edge but you cannot. So you, and everyone else, all people, try and try and try. Until one day, one of you succeeds. That person gets a hold of the edge and climbs up triumphantly. He looks to the other side, amazed and happy, and jumps off to taste those fruits. Then, after a while, someone else reaches the edge and climbs up. And so on. It is rare, but once in while, there is someone who looks down at the garden, and instead of jumping down, she decides to stay on the wall and extends her hands to others to help them to climb it too. That person is a Bodhisattva. They are in both worlds at the same time. They are here as guides and teachers.

We have all had a glimpse of enlightenment at some point in our lives. We are all Bodhisattvas to a certain extent. The following story from December 14, 2005, on the front page of the San Francisco Chronicle demonstrates our Bodhisattva nature.

There was a female humpback whale who became entangled in a spider web of crab traps and fishing lines just off the coast of San Francisco Bay. She was weighed down by hundreds of pounds of traps. She struggled to stay afloat. A fisherman (a Bodhisattva) spotted her and radioed an environmental group for help. When the rescue team (more Bodhisattvas) got there, they determined that the only way to untangle her was to dive in and do it manually. A few divers worked for hours around the whale with curved knives and eventually freed her.

When she was free, she swam around their boat in what seemed like joyous circles. Then she came up to each diver, one at a time, and nudged them. They said it was the most beautiful experience of their lives.

Let's reach a helping hand to others who may need our help. And they may not be human - whales or other animals – dogs, cats, crows, squirrels, snails, lizards, coyotes, or raccoons.

My wife, Theresa, traveled to Ecuador as part of a volunteer community education and conservation project. Her group stayed in the small villages of Loma Alta and El Suspiro conducting wildlife surveys and implementing a school program based on environmental awareness and conservation.

She remembers one boy who rode his old bike to school every morning. He would stand outside the windows of the weathered school building, simultaneously hopeful and embarrassed. His family did not have enough money to pay for the school. But he would stand outside and listen in through the open window. The teachers would occasionally shush him away, but most of the time allowed him to stay, taking pity on him.

When she returned from this trip, Theresa relayed the story of the boy to a few of our friends and family. All were moved by his desire to learn and saddened by his circumstances. How much do we take for granted? All of the many fortunate things we have!

The story of the boy deeply stirred Mary's heart. Being a long-time family friend, Mary requested more details. She obtained the boy's photo from Theresa's files, found his school, and the person who would be able to convey her concern for the boy.

It turns out that only $300 would pay for the whole school year. Mary followed through with her decision. That year, he went to school. Next year, and every year after, she is making a commitment of $300 to make that selfless donation.

It does not take much to be a Bodhisattva, but an open heart willing to feel compassion and extend our own kindness.

Enlightenment!...Then What?

Many of us experience moments of clarity, inner peace, and Oneness with the Universe. Few of us are able to sustain this Inner Peace on a continuous basis, although the underlying sense of Oneness is always there.

Have you ever wondered what happens to those individuals who have reached and sustained elated enlightened states for extended periods of time?

Once, a Buddhist monk walked to a far-away village to meet a renowned Buddhist master. He walked for many weeks. Upon reaching the village, he learned that the master lived on a high hill outside of the village. Excited to meet the master, he sped up the hill. On his way, he saw an old man walking down the hill with a heavy sack over his shoulders. As they approached each other, the student recognized the old man was the master he had been looking for. He stopped, kneeled, and bowed deeply in front of the man. *"Master, I have come a long way to meet you. I am so grateful to be here. I hope I may become your disciple and student. Master, what is it like to be enlightened?"*

The old man looked at him with caring eyes and a gentle smile. He dropped the heavy sack to the ground, straightened his back, stretched his shoulders, and took a deep breath. "Oh, that is what it's like," the student understood. "What happens next?" He inquired. The old man picked up the heavy sack, swung it around onto his shoulders, and continued down the hill.

Life goes on. A real yogi lives in two worlds. The physical world of material possessions and positions has to be attended to. It presents constant opportunities for growth and self-development, as well as illuminating the path for others. However, all actions are influenced by the knowledge of the underlying unity, by the sense of Inner Peace, and come from the place of Love and Compassion.

As we grow and capture more Light into our lives, we transition into becoming Karma Yogis, Bodhisattvas, whose role it is to help others.

NON-ATTACHMENT
Mess with Perfect

A Buddhist proverb states: "Everything is perfect with much room for improvement."

Another common phrase "Don't mess with Perfection" hints at the inherent 'perfection' present in any situation.

We often hear that things are as they should be, even if they seem hopeless sometimes.

However, in yoga, the recognition of that perfection is not enough. A yogi takes a proactive approach, and strives toward their peace of mind through multiple tools (meditation, acts of kindness, *Bhakti* or surrendering of ego through prayer, *Pratipaksha Bhavana* or seeing the positive in everything, and many more).

As a yogi, you may accept everything as already perfect, but in addition, you would ask yourself: "What can I do now to make my mind more at peace, less agitated, and more focused?"

With such a focused mind, you can be of greater service to others, instead of simply accepting things as they are. Sometimes, the Perfect has to be improved upon by making your mind more focused and at peace, and more useful to help those in need.

One of my teachers, Swami Satchidananda, used to say that "an action is perfect when it harms no one and brings benefit to at least one being." We can look at our actions through this lens.

Before you do something, before you step out the door, before you pick up your phone, or open your computer, ask yourself: "Will this make my mind more peaceful, and more focused? Will this help or harm others?"... and choose your actions accordingly.

How to Deal with Stress

One day, I was sitting outside and watching the trees sway in the wind. It was a windy day. The branches and leaves were tossed around in every direction.

I thought: what if the branches and the leaves had consciousness? Like us, they were conscious of their selves, and what if they had a plan, an expectation, to grow in a certain way, toward the sun.

Then, wind comes along, and starts dancing with them, bending them this way and that way. They would probably become very agitated with the wind. "No, I want to grow that way, I don't want to be bent this way," the trees would say. Imagine how much stress they would be in!

Yet, they are not. Instead, they allow, they go with the flow, with the wind and other elements.

How are we different? We are tossed around in every direction in our lives, and often against our plans, expectations, and desires. We refuse to bend, we resist, we fight under pressure, and sure enough we get stressed out.

It seems the crux of the problem with stress is having all these plans and expectations.

People, who take things lightly, who have no expectations of the outcomes, like the trees, welcoming any change that comes, are usually less stressed and more happy.

It seems that stress happens when the mind resists what is. What is here and now is different from how you expected it to be. Your plans, assumptions, expectations and desires get in the way of what is. If the present moment does not match any of these, you feel stressed.

How do you deal with it, using yoga? There are three yogic strategies of dealing with stress.

First, yoga wisdom tells us that we are not the mind. Just as much as we are not the physical body, which is only a vessel. If we see that the mind is only a wonderful tool, or a mechanism, that allows us to deal with the outside world and have experiences, but it is not who we are, we could break away from mental problems: plans, worries, fears, and expectations. These are all part of the mind, and if you are not the mind, then do not worry about being stressed. The mind is stressed, but YOU are not.

Next time, when your mind gets stressed, just say: OK, fine, let the mind be stressed, I know I am not the mind so I'll just watch it, let it do its thing.

This type of reasoning is called Discerning Intelligence (Buddhi), which helps us deal with stress through understanding what stress is. Often, we call it Non-Attachment: to the way things are, to outcomes, to any results of your actions, to any plans, or expectations. Instead, we learn to become a mindful witness of how the mind works.

Second, yoga wisdom teaches us to be in the present moment, and if you observe the present moment, you will discover that, in this moment, there are no expectations, plans, worries, assumptions, or even thoughts.

Clap your hands hard to make a sharp ringing sound. Now notice what thought you had in the very moment of the resounding clap.

Probably none. No thoughts, no stress.

Finally, we feel stressed because we own our expectations, assumptions, desires, and plans. These mental constructs are generally made up by our minds for our own benefit, meaning they are created for some personal selfish gain no matter how small. Here are some examples: we expect to catch our flight on time; we assume our life's partner will share our passions; we plan to make enough money to support ourselves and our children; we desire to be acknowledged, respected, and loved. All of these are common wishes. Yet, all of them contain a selfish core.

Yoga wisdom says that if we make our actions selfless, we would not attach to our expectations, assumptions, or plans. They are not ours anymore. If we are truly selfless, we catch a plane to go somewhere to be of service to others; our passion is lived for our family and friends, not only ourselves; and we make money to help others and to contribute to society. When our plans and desires do not work out, we do not take it personally – they were not intended for personal benefit from the beginning. Being selfless is the yogic way of living a stress-free life.

If you take a yoga class, you have a great opportunity to practice being stress free.

You can practice being present in the moment. You practice so you can have a healthy body and a peaceful mind – perfect tools for making a difference in the world. You can practice non-attachment to the outcome of the yoga class. If something comes out of it, great. If not, that is fine, too. Instead, focus on the process of practicing, on the process of breathing, the process of living, of working, of eating, and so on.

Apple Tree:
Non-Attachment

Non-attachment is a common theme in yoga and other spiritual traditions. It means not having personal or selfish desires. Instead, for peace of mind, yoga recommends to dedicate our actions and their results to benefit other human beings, animals, and the Earth. That is practicing Non-Attachment (*Vairagya* in Sanskrit).

In yoga philosophy there is an example of an apple tree which gives its fruits without expecting anything back. The apple tree is selfless. It's not attached to the results. If someone likes its apples, great. If someone doesn't like them, the tree does not get disturbed or lose its peace. If you throw a stone at the tree, it may give you even more apples.

We can learn from the apple tree. Imagine if you could do your work, just for the love of doing the work, and to benefit others.

I tried practicing that for a few days: not expecting how other people react to my work. Yet constantly, my mind interfered: "If someone does not come back or doesn't respond positively, does it mean they are not happy with my work." I could feel my mind was conditioned to be attached to the results, to worry and analyze people's reactions.

We cannot stop the mind from thinking. That is its job. But after a few days, I discovered that to keep the mind calm and free of worry, we must simply focus on our work in the present moment. Every moment. Moment to moment. Then, time disappears. Our actions become perfect and mindful. Our work becomes a selfless service and a form of meditation. That's when Non-Attachment is achieved.

The Artist

I was watching our three-year old son draw with chalk on his easel last night. He stood on a little stool and, with pursed-lip concentration, created circles, lines, and shapes of different colors. As any parents would think of their children, my wife and I thought it was genius. His art pieces looked deliberate, some with precise lines that required the tongue to stick out, and others with crazy messy free-hand of a true artist.

The most amazing part to me was not the art, but the ease and complete non-attachment with which he got rid of it. As soon as the chalk board space was filled, our son would promptly, without pausing, put his chalk down and take his open palms to the board, wiping it clean.

"But wait!" my wife and I would exclaim, *"Let's marvel at it. Let's take a photo."* But it was too late. His palms encrusted with chalk, he would start the process all over, creating another masterpiece only to erase its existence few minutes later.

For him, the fun was in the process, not the finished product. He did not care to look at it later, to take a picture of it, or tell others. He did not require praise or recognition. His ego did not need a boost. He took as much delight in erasing it as in creating it. A three-year old can do that effortlessly.

We, grownups, tend to lose that effortless ability to enjoy the process and not seek credit for our work. Yet, we get the most out of our work or art when we require no praise for it, when we expect nothing, and just do it without attachments or expectations. If we do not put a condition of "If I get this right, then I will be …" or "If I do this well, then I will get…" – then we retain our inner happiness independent of anything else. Working this way, invested in the process and not the outcome, is the real way to happiness.

Good Thing, Bad Thing, Who Knows?
(a story of unknown origin)

There once was a farmer who owned a horse and had one son. One day, his horse ran away. The neighbors came to express their concern: *"Oh, that's too bad. How are you going to work the fields now?"* The farmer replied: *"Good thing, Bad thing, Who knows?"*

In a few days, his horse came back and brought another horse with her. Now, the neighbors were glad: *"Oh, how lucky! Now you can do twice as much work as before!"* The farmer replied: *"Good thing, Bad thing, Who knows?"*

The next day, the farmer's son fell off the new horse and broke his leg. The neighbors were concerned again: *"Now that he is incapacitated, he can't help you around, that's too bad."* The farmer replied: *"Good thing, Bad thing, Who knows?"*

Soon, the news came that a war broke out, and all the young men in the country were required to join the army. The villagers were sad because they knew that many of their young men would not come back. The farmer's son could not be drafted into the army because of his broken leg. His neighbors were envious: *"How lucky! You get to keep your only son."* The farmer replied: *"Good thing, Bad thing, Who knows?"*

The story illustrates ancient wisdom to reserve judgment, practice non-attachment (to results or outcomes) and remain in the present moment to avoid stress and worry.

What's Right With This Picture

We learn to be critical from a young age. Critical thinking is a good quality in today's world, and encouraged at educational institutions starting with preschool. It makes one more analytical and better at problem-solving and decision-making.

A less desirable side effect of critical thinking is that we tend to see only the negative side of things – so we can fix it somehow. Children are given two similar pictures with one of them having slight differences, or things that are out of place (wrong things), and they are asked to find them: What's wrong with this picture?

We learn to see the world through the same critical lens. What's wrong with this situation? What's wrong with this person? And so on. Instead, we need to train our critical minds to pick out the good things in every situation, too. It's a great practice to teach kids. And it's a great yogic practice to develop a habit to see the good things and the right things in everything.

In every situation, there is a lesson to be learned. In every picture you see, there is something right about it, probably more than just one thing.

Think about a situation from today. At work. At the bank. At the store. Anywhere else you went to today. Or even at home.

What's good about that place? What's right about it? What's right with the picture you are looking at right now?

In yoga, we call this *Pratipaksha Bhavana* – the habit of seeing the positive in life, or substituting the positive for any negative.

Another reason to develop the attitude of *Pratipaksha Bhavana* is to deal with stress. When we think about a situation or a person critically, we expect certain outcomes: we want it to be the 'right' way and immediately criticize the 'wrong' in it. When our expectations are not met, we feel stressed. Instead, when you see the good in everything, stress is reduced, if not completely vanished.

Story of Narada.
What's More Important:
Practice or Non-Attachment

Narada is a sage in Hindu philosophy whose responsibility is o spread wisdom, and support yogis and aspirants on their spiritual quest to Self-Realization. He travels in his chariot between our physical world and the astral world of enlightened beings. This is a story of Narada as told by Swami Satchidananda in his book *The Yoga Sutras of Patanjali: Translation and Commentary*.[10]

One day, Narada was riding through a forest and spotted an old yogi sitting in meditation in front of his cave. The yogi saw Narada, too, and got up to greet him. He then asked: *"Narada, are you by chance going to see Krishna?"* (Krishna represents Absolute Consciousness).

"Sure, I probably will." Narada replied.

"Would you mind asking Krishna on my behalf, how many more lifetimes I have left until Enlightenment?"

"Yes, I can do that for you."

As he continued through the same forest, he came upon another yogi. This one was standing under a giant tree, singing and dancing, the expression of joy on his face. Narada stopped to observe and wonder.

When the man noticed him, he came over to greet him as well.

"Hi Narada, may I help you with anything?"

"No, thank you, but if you like I can ask Krishna about your progress. I am going to see Him soon."

"Sure, that is fine," the man responded.

Narada left, and years went by. One day, traveling in the same forest, Narada found the first yogi. Still there, sitting in the same spot, the yogi sprang up to his feet when he saw Narada.

"Narada!" He ran over excitedly. *"Where have you been all these years? Tell me, what did Krishna say?"*

"Krishna said that you only have four more lifetimes left until you become enlightened."

The smile left the yogi's face.

"What!" He said incredulously, *"That cannot be! I've been here for fifty years. I have dedicated my whole life to finding enlightenments. Surely, it has to be in this lifetime. I cannot wait four more! That's just not fair. That's it. I give up."*

With that, the yogi walked away. Narada shrugged his shoulders, and continued on.

As he reached the big tree, he saw the other yogi. Still there, still dancing and singing and feeling joyous, he smiled at Narada in recognition. Narada walked over, put his hand on the yogi's shoulder and said:

"You see this big tree? Can you count the number of leaves on this tree?"

"Yes, sure, I have time – I can count."

"Krishna said that the number of leaves on this tree is the number of lives you have left until Enlightenment."

Upon hearing the words, the yogi's face lit up in astonishment.

"Wow!" He exclaimed joyously. *"You mean that even for me it's possible? I thought you were going to say the leaves of the whole forest!"* He became so ecstatic, that he attained Self-Realization right in that moment. Narada smiled and waved him on.

"Come on! It looks like there is no need to wait, you are ready now!"

The moral of the story is that non-attachment to the outcome is more important than practice itself. You can meditate for fifty years, you can practice all day, but if you are still attached to certain expectations and results, they bind you and real progress eludes you. Don't we know people who take yoga classes, yet they treat others in selfish ways?

Being Present and Mindfulness
Driving in India, and Staying Present

One must have a lot of patience in India and find a way of dealing with constant sensory overload. For this reason, it must have developed to be such a spiritual place, to escape the mayhem of the loud smelly crowded streets.

The idea of time and personal space is very different in India. Walking or driving through the streets is an assault on the senses. People, cars, bikes, tuk-tuks, goats and cows, with so many colors and so much noise. The smells, good and bad, are overpowering.

Just the sound of traffic alone can drive anyone crazy. Drivers aren't shy about using their horns. The honking is constant. After a few minutes, one wants to run away to a quiet temple. Or find that quiet place inside. That is why it needs to be a spiritual place. You have to have a strong sense of inner balance to deal with so many distractions.

My friend Prakash and I drove from Chennai to Pondicherry, about three hours away. In the beginning, as we weaved our way through congested streets of Chennai, our driver Ramu kept on the horn about every ten seconds. At first it was kind of amusing as we were just part of this big moving mess. But as we left the city and the roads cleared, with only a few cars and people around, Ramu's honking did not stop. That's when it got annoying.

I asked my friend why Ramu was still honking. We were in the countryside. No more traffic. Why honk? Prakash asked Ramu in Tamil, the local language, and in the few minutes that followed, Ramu tried hard to beep less. Apparently, he was warning potential road hazards, kids playing, dogs, goats, and cows wandering out onto the road, and other drivers. That made sense but still was aggravating, especially when there was no one on the road.

I could see that Ramu did it without actually looking around. It was a reflex action for him. Prakash and I wondered if he did it to keep himself awake.

So I watched myself getting annoyed. I noticed the real reason I was annoyed was that I would start day-dreaming and the sharp sound of the horn would bring me back and interrupt my thoughts. I thought to myself: there is no way to get around it, so why fight it, why don't I use this sound the way Zen meditation teachers use a loud sound, or a wooden stick to whack their students, as a way to bring them to the present moment?

Every time Ramu honked, I took a slow breath, and sent myself a mental note to relax, and notice the scenery outside the car window. This went on for a while. Honk! … Breathe, relax, notice …

If Ramu took a long time to honk, I became aware that I was actually looking forward to the next honk. It became a positive trigger, instead of an annoying sound. I stayed in the moment, breathing, relaxing, and watching the green hills and ramshackle houses rolling by without getting caught up in my thoughts, and without judgment. I turned it into a tool to stay in the present moment.

In a yoga class, and in other similar situations, we get caught up in our thoughts, likes, and dislikes. We can also find a similar tool. A distant car alarm could serve as a trigger to take a slow breath, relax, and find where you are in that moment. Or someone sneezing, or a cell phone, or anything else that potentially can become annoying to you. Make it a trigger to be present. That way you will retain your peace of mind. And that's practicing Yoga.

Spider on a Blade of Grass:
Continuous Awareness

Once meditating outside, I noticed a small orange spider on my knee. I carefully set it on a blade of grass and watched it for a minute.

The spider ran up to the edge but did not jump. Instead, it stopped and stuck a couple of its legs out into the space beyond the blade of grass as if testing new territory. Then it hopped over to the next blade of grass. It continued to move in the same manner, testing first, then jumping over.

That is how we should practice. Approach your edges carefully. Pause. Breathe. Get comfortable. And the next blade of grass may happen automatically.

The most important element is continuous awareness. Asking the question: *How do I feel right now?*

When we learn, or do, something new, that is how we feel: bumping into our edges of ability and comfort. Hang out there – at the edge – for today. Or longer. Until you have learned, or feel so comfortable that the edge has moved out further, and you find yourself on the next blade of grass – at the next level of practice.

There are also emotional and psychological edges of which we must be mindful. Sometimes, it is just as important to recognize that certain edges will not, and should not, be jumped over. Or else, you may find yourself in a vulnerable situation that you are not ready to accept. The most important aspect, again, is continuous awareness: How do I feel right now? Can I stay here and breathe?

On Mount Laguna:
State of Presence

We waited for the sun to set. Then we hiked back to the cars. We had a lot to carry back, mostly equipment from filming outside all day. It took about an hour to go back.

It was getting dark very fast, and somehow I got ahead of the video crew. So I decided to sit and wait for them. I sat on my bag right on the trail.

I was in the middle of a huge grassy field surrounded by mountains and forest. The grass was about two feet tall and it swayed with the wind in waves and circles. There was a dark silhouette of a mountain in front of me, and right above it, in the purple sky, was a single star. It was so incredibly bright. It may have been Sirius or the North Star.

The forest felt quiet yet alive. I could see bats flying through the air. And I could hear crickets singing in the distance. I could detect the fragrance of the desert in the air, with countless flower blossoms dissolved into it. For a few moments, I was immersed in the experience.

Then something curious started to happen. I found myself saying: *"OK, this is really beautiful. Look at that mountain there. Look at the star and the sky. See the bats flying. Smell the desert, and so on."* My mind started to narrate what I was experiencing. So consciously I had to tell my mind to stop it, to let go, and just be.

I found the present moment again. But soon, the mind switched back on: *"What if there are coyotes in the grass? Or maybe there are deer? I wonder if I could hear them or even see them."* I stopped the mind once again, and just told myself to be. This went on: from being present to being mental, then back to being present. Until the film crew found me on the trail.

This kind of mental chatter happens all the time to all of us. We are living in the mind rather than in the present moment. It is possible to spend the whole day immersed completely in your thoughts. There are times when it's OK to do that. But that's really not living, not being alive.

Yoga practice gives us the time to notice this restless nature of the mind. It's normal to get distracted and get involved in the mental monologue. As we progress in our yoga practice, we begin to spend more time in the state of presence and pure awareness – our natural state.

If it happens during a yoga class, catch yourself doing it, and try to draw yourself out by asking yourself: Where is my body right now? What is my body telling me right now? How far to stretch? How much to let go? How fully to breathe?

What about right now? Can you be present at this time? What's your posture like? Is your breath flowing? Can you feel your heartbeat? The warmth of your body? How do you feel in your heart center, in your gut center, in your third eye/intuition center?

Rest your mental focus on what is happening now for a minute. Ask yourself some of the above questions and feel (do not think about) the answers.

A Lesson From Thoreau

I drove to Walden Pond to go for a hike. Getting out of the car, my hand habitually reached for the cell phone. I started to place it in my pocket, and suddenly thought: Why do I need my cell phone on a hike? What business do I have to do on the phone when I am hiking and enjoying nature? I remembered Henry David Thoreau's words, who wrote about a similar experience, except he didn't have a cell phone or modern technology to get away from. I had to smile about it because it seemed more than coincidental that what he wrote took place right here, at Walden Pond. Maybe these woods evoke a sense of awe and Oneness with nature.

Here's what Thoreau wrote:[12]

"Of course it is of no use to direct our steps to the woods, if they do not carry us thither. I am alarmed when it happens that I have walked a mile into the woods bodily, without getting there in spirit. In my afternoon walk I would feign forget all my morning occupations and my obligations to society. But it sometimes happens that I cannot easily shake off the village. The thought of some work will run in my head and I am not where my body is – I am out of my senses. In my walks I would feign return to my senses. What business have I in the woods, if I am thinking of something out of the woods? …Above all, we cannot afford not to live in the present."

– Henry David Thoreau, 1854

Isn't it amazing what he wrote back then? What business do we have in the past or the future when life and happiness demand that we stay in the present?

Life happens in the present. Happiness is experienced in the present. Especially outdoors.

There are times in the day for self-reflection, and analyzing your past actions, and planning your future events. But these should be attended to fully, when needed, not while you are practicing yoga on the mat, walking in the woods, or being mindful in your daily actions.

Like many of us, I too multi-task, become distracted, and allow the ego to get in the way. There is no use feeling bad about it. Instead, I stick to Buddha's advice: *"Just do your best."*

As far as yoga practice goes, we all try to stay present. If you catch your thoughts drifting into the past or the future, come back. Notice where the body is, where the breath is...

Cat's Kapalabhati

If you have ever had cats, you know that cats' bodies are very flexible. They do not store much tension. They can sit still for hours.

One of our cats named Chucho meditates on the windowsill every morning. I watch him from my yoga mat out of the corner of my eye, but he is as still as can be and does not move.

I am sure he watches me, too. I usually do a few rounds of Kapalabhati (forceful exhalations also known as the Skull-Shining Breath) which catches Chucho's attention because Kapalabhati is a series of short sharp sounds. Every time he hears me, he turns and looks in disdain for interrupting his silent focus.

One day, I sit up to get ready for my breathing practice, when suddenly, I hear "Hmm… Hmmm… Hmm.." coming from the windowsill. Sounds like the Kapalabhati breath. My first thought: "Chucho?! Did the cat learn to do the breath? He's heard it many times from me." I turn to look at him – he is coughing up a hairball!

I smile. After a moment, he is done. Like nothing happened, he goes back to the window, perfectly still and present. He reminds me of how to be present, too.

To Become Still, Witness Movement

We want to have a calm and peaceful mind. Often, the mind is too active. So we have this polarity within our being: on one end, there is noise, activity, movement, the body is moving, the mind is always moving (yoga calls the mind a drunken monkey stung by a scorpion or a snake with a thousand heads, trying to be everywhere at the same time); and on the other end, there is stillness, silence, consciousness. It's interesting to have a conscious experience of this polarity. The funny thing is that it is a conscious choice to be still. It's very simple and accessible to anyone. To become still, you only have to notice movement. Because only from a relatively still point can you detect movement. We cannot see movement if we are moving ourselves. The more subtle the movement that we observe, the more still and conscious we become.

I had such an experience at a yoga party at a friend's place in San Diego. We had a lot of food and people brought musical instruments. After eating, we sat in a circle and made a lot of noise, drumming, singing, and dancing. At one point, I was sitting on the floor with my eyes closed, and suddenly, I became really still. I felt as though I was in a hurricane. Everything was spinning and moving, but I was in the center where it was perfectly still. I watched all that movement: sound of the drums, people's voices, my own breath, my heartbeat, my stomach digesting food, and even my thoughts. Then I consciously got involved in the movement again - I started chanting. And then I played with this polarity: getting involved, then witnessing, and getting involved again.

I like to use the image of being in the still center of a hurricane, or the center of a spinning top. By choice, you can become still and peaceful. Only notice movement.

Begin with your breath moving – notice it. Notice the body making its own subtle adjustments. Your heartbeat. Your thoughts.

Witness Energy

Once in a yoga class, I noticed a tiny flea-fly twirling wild in the same spot. It stayed low to the ground and spun wildly. I wondered: Why?

Then, I looked around the class, and everyone was doing a twisting pose, moving, fidgeting. I thought to myself: if an intelligent alien saw us right now, they may also ask: Why?

The same can be asked of many things. Take soccer for instance. Twelve grown men chase a ball around a big field. Spectators get so enthralled and heated up about this game that they are ready to fight for their soccer teams as can be seen in some countries. An alien can look at the game of soccer and definitively determine that human beings are crazy. What a waste of energy!

Yet, isn't everything just an expression of energy? We give meaning to it. Our minds must give meaning to everything we do, to rationalize our actions. But in Absolute Reality, it's just nature expressing itself: yoga, soccer, your work. Pure energy. Like the flea-fly.

We learn in yoga to witness it. First, observe the body and its energy as it moves, and breathes, and performs a myriad of its internal actions. Then, observe the mind – analyzing, reasoning, getting distracted, and focusing. Our practice is to witness both, body and mind, without getting involved. Just like watching the flea-fly.

Nature's Cycles and
Our Internal Cycles

Traveling in Virginia and North Carolina in early September, I observed many weather patterns. It was just before and during a hurricane. Sunny and humid turned to rainy and windy and cooler than normal, and then back to sunny and humid. The cycles of nature rolled in with intensity, and I was made acutely aware of the constant flux in nature.

When there is congestion or blockage, nature cleanses itself, as in a hurricane. The cleanse is often violent.

Our body is like nature. It goes through cycles all the time. Sometimes, there is congestion, and cleansing is necessary. Yoga is a practice of purification and deals with multi-level cleansing. Our body and mind go through cycles physically, emotionally, and mentally, and cleanse at each of those levels.

To practice yoga is to witness these cycles and changes and remain a witness without judgment. With courage and patience, explore and invite the experience of change and cleansing, allow it to happen and observe with compassionate detachment.

Being in the Moment
With Nothing To Do

What happens when, all of a sudden, you have nothing to do? You find something to do. If you are used to having a full schedule, making yourself involved and busy, and then – nothing. What does your mind do? What happens when you sit down to meditate? All these thoughts rush in.

We went away to a town of Idyllwild in the San Jacinto mountains for a weekend. We hiked in the morning, but in the afternoon, we had no plans. So we just walked around town without purpose, watching birds, squirrels, and people. And I found my mind constantly asking: OK, what are we doing next? What's next on the agenda?

And there, in the mountains, there was nothing next.

It took a little effort to not do anything. I had to tell my mind: Just be. Be in the moment. And as the day went on, I kept noticing this tendency to be restless, and continued placing the mind back into the present. That became my practice while being there.

The same happens in a yoga class – the mind constantly wanders away from the present. Any time you notice that your mind is getting ahead, planning what you are going to do after the class, or just anticipating the next move, bring it to this moment. We have two tools: the breath and the body – they are always in the moment.

Good Quiet Times Doing Nothing

We are, as a culture, addicted to being thrilled. We constantly seek excitement. Our minds seek to be engaged and stimulated. We can thank the media, the advertising industry, digital technology, and the pressure to 'make it' to keep up with the changing world for our need for mental stimulation.

Every day must bring something 'worth' living for. As if it does not already. But we feel that we must strive for something more. Every night, most of us plan to do 'something,' whether it's watching suspenseful movies or comedy shows, going out to a club or a restaurant, or going for a drive or a walk among other people.

This is perfectly fine, of course. But what happens to our nervous system, and our adrenal glands, if they are stimulated all the time without a restful break? The nervous system gets frazzled. The adrenal glands get shot.

After a while, we may start feeling the effects: chronic anxiety, constant worry, easy fatigue, sudden fears (that may not be typical to our selves like the fear of traveling or heights), insomnia, and so on.

What if we took time to do nothing? Nothing exciting, that is. Does that sound boring?

What if we just spend a day or an evening quietly? Simply sitting and listening to our selves. Without TV, loud music, phone conversations, emails, or big dinners with lots of people.

What if we could inhale deeply and exhale all of our plans and expectations of this moment?

This way, we can consciously press the pause button of our tendency for stimulation, recharge our nervous system, and reduce the noise in the mind.

Mind Your Business

My friend Joel teaches Thai Massage and visits Thailand every year. He loves the Thai culture, and converted to Thai Buddhism years ago. We were in Thailand together once, and every day he visited a wat, a Thai temple, to meditate. Because he knew a lot of the monks at the temple, he offered them Thai Massage. They loved it.

In a wat, there is a certain code of ethics to be observed and respected by everyone. One cannot, for example, wear shoes or shorts inside, no cell phones, no loud talking. Yet every time, my friend would see people "breaking" the rules. It bothered him a little. On this one day he decided to complain to the head monk.

He went over and asked: *"Master, why don't you enforce the rules? Maybe we should have a sign or have one of the monks as an attendant."*

After hearing this, the head monk looked at my friend very sternly for a few seconds, and then got visibly angry: *"Don't you worry about other people and what they are doing! Mind your own actions! Don't allow your mind to get disturbed with others. It's not your business. It's their actions, their karma. Are you in the moment when you think of that? ... Go and meditate!"*

My friend didn't expect this reaction from the all-loving monk. But immediately he saw his point. He was completely involved in judging and criticizing others.

When he told me this story, I thought of myself in a yoga class, being judgmental. Don't we all get like that, looking around, comparing and judging: *"Oh, her knees aren't as straight as they should be,"* or *"He is doing it wrong,"* and so on. That's how our mind is. It is conditioned to compare and find fault.

After Joel's story, every time I notice someone breaking the rules at a temple, or in a yoga class, I ask myself: Am I in the moment? Or am I judging? It became a useful tool. As soon as I catch my mind being critical, I ask: Where is my breath? What is my action right now?

SELF-DISCIPLINE
Self-Discipline:
Tapas

Yoga practice has always been about self-discipline. Ancient yogis designed ways to challenge themselves physically and mentally. They adhered to strict practices for extended periods of time to challenge their mind and gain control over its nature. Some of these practices have been very austere and challenging like walking around a mountain for a week without food (Mount Kailash is one such place) or meditating on a wind-swept cliff for days on end, while other practices have been more moderate and have made their way into our modern life: cleansing, fasting, regular community service, and meditation.

The concept of self-discipline is central in yoga. Yogis call this *Tapas*, or *Tapasya*, which translates as "to burn" and implies the "burning, or purifying, of the ego, and its egocentric tendencies," through the means of performing challenging practices that put the mind against its own limits.

We do not have to sit naked on a mountaintop to practice Tapas. A simple practice like giving up coffee or sugar for a week is challenging enough for many people, and would put your mind to a test. The question is: Who is really in control: your willpower - the *Buddhi*, or your ego?

The three criteria for a *Tapas* practice:

162

1. It must be doable. If quitting coffee for a week is not doable for you right now, try for three days instead, or choose a different practice like starting each day with a ten-minute silent meditation.

2. It must be specific. Set the terms of your practice as specifically as possible. For example, ten minutes of meditation, between 6:00 a.m. and 6:30 a.m., for one full week.

3. It must be trackable. It's best to write it down and track your progress every day. You can do it on a piece of paper or your smartphone. Put a checkmark next to each day that you accomplish your Tapas. Tracking your accomplishment gives you strength to keep going and helps gain more control over the mind.

Years ago, I spent a month in Mexico at a yoga retreat with a renowned yogi from the Integral Yoga School, Swami Asokananda. Swamiji and I ended up sharing a palm-frond-roofed casita due to limited space at the retreat center. It was a great experience for me to observe the daily habits and rituals of a committed yogi with over thirty years of practice. His day was all structured around Tapas practices.

Swami Asokananda ate only once a day – at lunch. He meditated for an hour three times a day, at six in the morning, at noon before lunch, and at sunset. He would have Pranayama for "dinner" – various breathing practices meant to rejuvenate the body, restore its vital life-force (Prana), and prepare the mind for meditation. Swamiji practiced Alternate Nostril Breathing for forty-five minutes each day at sunset withholding his breath (comfortably) for shockingly long periods of time, twenty seconds after each inhalation and after each exhalation. These were a few of his many Tapas practices, all intended to establish firm control over the body and mind.

Here are some other suggestions:

- fast for 36 hours on water or liquids (dinner to breakfast);
- become a vegetarian for a week;
- practice 20 minutes of yoga asanas for a week on your own in the morning before breakfast;
- perform a deep breathing practice for 15 minutes for a week at a set time every day;
- perform one selfless compassionate act per day for a week, even as   simple as a smile at a stranger, or picking up trash on the road;
- spend 5 minutes each morning naming everything you are grateful for in your life, for a week;
- tell the people you love that you love them every day for a week.

My Cold Training

Tapas is an important part of a yogi's lifestyle and practice. When I first learned about *Tapas*, I became very committed to several such practices. I kept a *Tapas* journal, and tracked my daily commitment. With time, many simple practices, like drinking two full glasses of water before breakfast in the morning, became part of my lifestyle. I do not need to track these practices anymore as I used to. I do them naturally like brushing teeth. However, from time to time, I still set up a *Tapas* practice that challenges me.

A couple of years ago, I read a book about the Iceman,[13] a man named Wim Hof, famous for controlling his body temperature at will. Apparently, he has been monitored by scientists in ice-cold water tanks, where he manages not only to maintain his normal body temperature but increase it after 15-20 minutes of being submerged. He has also run a marathon above the Arctic Circle wearing only shorts. And similarly, he hiked Mount Everest.

What piqued my interest was his control of the body through his will. His story reminded me of the Himalayan yogis and Tibetan monks living in cold harsh conditions at high altitudes. Many of them do not wear much clothing. There are well-documented cases of monks and yogis controlling their body temperature at will by the use of certain breathing and visualization techniques. The tales of Tibetan monks were common - sitting naked in the snow on windy mountains with wet sheets on their shoulders, and drying those wet sheets with their body heat, steam rising off their bodies.

There are such techniques in yoga, collectively known as the Yoga of Inner Fire. These techniques help one drive internal body heat to the extremities and remain comfortable in sub-zero conditions.

The book inspired me. I knew the techniques and practiced them occasionally but never long enough to really feel their lasting effect, or test them in a really cold environment. Living in New England at the time, I decided that, starting in November, I would go outside when the temperature was under 40 degrees Fahrenheit, rain or shine or snow or blustery wind, and sit on my towel for thirty minutes practicing the Yoga of Inner Fire.

I decided to treat the whole practice as *Tapas*, track it and stick to it all winter long. I would only wear my shorts.

It turned out to be a cold winter that year. I sat in sleeting rain, snow blizzards also known as Nor'easters, and negative windchill temperatures.

The initial shock of the cold on the skin was the worst of it. Stepping out, getting to my spot outside, and getting comfortable in a seated position took the most determination. Once I was seated, I focused on my internal warmth. The vital organs always maintain the same temperature. I would relax my muscles, and concentrate on driving that internal warmth out to my skin.

My main techniques were *Kapalabhati* (skull-shining, or fire breath), *Uddhyana Bandha* (stomach energy lock), *Agnisar Dhauti* (fire cleansing of the stomach), *Kumbhakas* (breath retention), and *Bhavana* (visualization of energy flow). The more I practiced, the easier it became, and the shorter it took to get really warm. After a couple of weeks of practice, it would take me just about a minute to feel very comfortable outside. My muscles would relax. Goose bumps disappeared. I would feel a pleasant tingling sensation of warmth pulsing through the blood vessels and the skin. It felt electric.

I was warm and comfortable enough to stand up and walk around the yard. My neighbors probably thought I was insane, but it felt exhilarating and energizing. The sense of warmth and electricity remained for the next couple of hours. It actually felt strange to have to wear clothing once back inside. When the warm weather returned in the spring, I switched to taking cold showers, and swimming at Walden Pond.

The Focus of A Cat

One morning I went outside as usual to do my practice. In the middle of the lawn, there sat a neighborhood cat. He sat very still and tall, staring at the grass. "Looking for gofers again," I thought to myself.

Then, I proceeded to my spot and started my practice: about a half hour of yoga asanas, Tai Chi and Qi Gong exercises, fifteen minutes of breathing exercises, and then about twenty minutes of meditation. After the meditation, I opened my eyes and got up to leave, picking up my towel. Then I looked over and saw the cat again. He had not moved from the spot, very still and focused just as before. "Still meditating," I thought to myself. "He will surely get what he wants. Those poor gofers." Then I realized how incredible was his patience and determination to achieve his goal. He was here before I came and was still here. I thought, this is the kind of focus, one-pointed attention, that we, people, need in our actions, especially when attempting to meditate.

Nothing else matters to the cat at the moment; he is not disturbed by analyzing the past and planning the future. He is just here and now. I thought, next time I sit down to meditate, I will think of the cat, and remember his patience. Even if it is only twenty minutes, nothing else should matter. The same is true for all other actions, like playing sports, dancing, playing music, and practicing yoga. We need to cultivate being present. This is how it is supposed to be practiced. Total unwavering focus.

How to Bear Insult —
Power of Non-Reactivity

Once a begging saint was approached by a man on the street. The man decided to test the sage: "Hey! You are just a fake! Stop pretending!"

The saint did not appear to hear the man.

"You hear me? You fake!" Again, the saint did not seem affected. Now the man yelled angrily: "Hey! Are you deaf? Can't you hear me?!"

The saint turned to him and smiled: "Yes, I can hear you very well." "Why don't you respond to what I am saying? I am calling you a fake."

The saint spoke: "Dear sir, suppose you brought me some fruits, and I did not want to eat them, what would you do?"

"Well, I would just take the fruits back." The man answered.

"In the same way, I do not enjoy all the things you have brought me now, so you can just take it back," the saint explained.

Yogis have always treated it as the highest spiritual practice (Sadhana) to bear insult with a serene mind. To develop the power of non-reactivity and simply remain a witness like the saint in the story. If you do not like what is offered to you, do not take it. If flowery words of praise make us happy, and insults upset us, our minds are not yet strong.

Swami Sivananda, a 20th-century saint, has been known to say *"one of the highest Sadhanas is to bear insult without returning it."*

Another way is to actually welcome insult and pain as purification of the ego. This practice is known as another kind of a Tapas practice as also purifies the ego.

Thank the person offending you. They come into your life as a teacher, too. Feel the emotional "burn" of the insult and accept it as purification. In fact, you may even ask for more – then you will really puzzle the offender.

Don't Walk Away

Yoga wisdom tells us that for peace of mind, one should disregard any wickedness in people. Any rude, wicked behavior should be ignored. Often, people interpret this message as avoiding a bad situation altogether. Indeed, sometimes that is exactly what we need to do to retain our peace of mind – to avoid and walk away from an inevitable collision.

Here is a story told by the modern-day sage, Swami Satchidananda, in his book *The Yoga Sutras of Patanjali*, about a sparrow who builds a cozy nest and takes comfort in it during a heavy rainstorm. As he enjoys the warmth inside, he looks out and sees a monkey sitting on the same branch, totally drenched and shivering in the cold rain.

The sparrow, feeling cheeky and confident, calls out: *"Hey, aren't you one of the smartest animals? Why don't you build yourself a shelter?"*

The monkey looks over angrily, hops over to the nest, and smashes it into pieces. The poor sparrow barely escapes and now must sit in the cold rain without shelter.

The moral of the story is that "sometimes we come across such monkeys in our life, and it's best to just ignore them. Good advice only angers them."

Have you ever told someone to stop smoking, or start a yoga practice, only to get into an argument?

However, to walk away is not always the best strategy. Disregarding the wicked also implies something else: to not buy into the wicked behavior, but act in a completely opposite, mostly loving and compassionate, way.

If you drive, you may have come across angry drivers. People driving get caught up in acts of trivial self-importance that can turn into unfortunate outcomes. In the big scheme of things, none of those driving altercations matter. What if you smiled at an angry driver? What if you rolled down your window and said sincerely: "Have a wonderful day!"

Chances are, the driver would realize how ridiculous they are acting. Typically, an angry driver expects you to do the same: roll down your window and flip them off, or say something unsavory, and speed away. Instead, you choose not to buy into that behavior – disregard it – and act in an unexpectedly kind way. It can stop them right away. It makes light of the situation, and shows how immaterial it is.

One day, my wife and I walked into a sandwich shop for a quick lunch in another town. As we ordered and sat down, we noticed two teenage girls sitting at a table across from ours. There was also a family of four with two young children, and a couple of other customers. One of the teenage girls was on the phone speaking loudly for everyone to hear. The other girl was sitting with a grimace and rolling her eyes at what was being said. The girl on the phone could not have been more profane. The F word was spicing up every phrase and every sentence. The worst of it, she was screaming so we all could hear her, including the kids whose parents looked down and whispered quietly shaking their heads.

Before my wife could stop me, I was up on my feet and over at the girls' table.

"Excuse me," I said and smiled. The girls pretended not to hear me.

"Excuse me!" much louder this time, I smiled again as they turned to look at me with dropped jaws, *"Could you take your conversation outside please? There are other people here."* I stated firmly.

"Wait a sec!" the phone girl said into the phone and got up to face me. She was no more than seventeen, well-dressed, attractive, makeup and hair done, and seething with rage. *"What the f... did you say?!"* she screamed inches away from my face.

I observed my initial impulse to get away, or push her away. Probably what she expected me to do. I also observed myself getting hot, and took a deep breath. That breath interrupted my impulsive response, and I heard myself say to the girl: *"You look like a good person... Your hair looks good. You are an attractive girl...(pause)"*

She and her friend were both staring at me confused in disbelief.

"I was just asking if you girls would take that conversation outside." I smiled kindly looking straight into her eyes.

Something softened inside her. Her humanity awoke and she dropped her gaze. Her anger was gone. *"Let's go."* She said to her friend and stormed out of the shop.

As I returned to our table, my wife asked: *"What did you say to her?"*

Sometimes it takes courage, self-control, and a deep breath to resist the temptation to flee a sticky situation, or get sucked into the same negative behavior. But walking away may not be the best way to deal with it, or affect positive change in the world. To disregard the wicked means to disregard the behavior - not the person. Even a wicked person may have kindness hidden deep within.

PLAYFULNESS, DELIGHT, & CELEBRATION
Delight in Other's Virtues

In the famous American classic *The Great Gatsby*, the main character is reminded right in the beginning of the novel that there are people who have been less fortunate than he, to be humble and appreciate what he has.

To take it a step further, it is a great practice to appreciate the virtues of other people.

When you meet or hear about someone very talented, generous, beautiful, or wealthy in any way, what is your initial reaction?

People's virtue, talent, success, or fortune, may come in many ways. Athletic, physical, intellectual, musical, financial.

Yoga wisdom suggests that we develop a sense of delight toward others' virtues. When you are sincerely delighted about someone else's success, you multiply your own sense of happiness. You can find a dozen people every day who feel blessed and fortunate. If you feel fortunate with them, for them, you raise your own feeling of inner joy.

This world is an energetic universe. When someone has a positive feeling from their success or accomplishment, they elevate their energy field, and they are more likely to do good in the world. If we tune it to that good vibe, we elevate our own energy field and are also more likely to continue doing good.

Next time you meet someone fortunate, successful, generous, or compassionate, remember that they are elevating the energy balance of the Universe.

The Importance of Being Playful

A friend and I were standing outside discussing some sort of plan, when all of a sudden, we saw a young woman skipping up the street. We paused as she skipped by, looked at each other quizzically, and smiled. Immediately, we felt a sense of lightness and playfulness.

We don't see many grown-ups skipping around, or being playful in other ways. I think we forget how good it feels to be playful, and how much it affects others if we are playful around them. It sends a happy ripple into the world. We need more playfulness.

There is always time for being serious and somber. No doubt about that. But playfulness seems to be overlooked.

What if we all make a point to be playful at least once each day? We could make it a simple *Tapas* practice to be playful once a day for a month.

You do it among friends and family at first, before you take it out to the public.

Shimmy your shoulders when you talk to someone. Do a dance move whenever possible.

Skip down a grocery store aisle, or do an arabesque to pick something off a shelf. Smile at strangers. Sing out loud when driving, or walking.

Exaggerate any positive reaction – jump with your arms in the air upon hearing good news, shout "Yes!" or "Nice!" or some other positive expletive.

Use your body, your eyes, and your speech to be playful. I guarantee you it will lighten up your day, and may lighten up the day for those around you.

Boogie-Woogie:
How to Feel Good

What makes us happy is to boogie-woogie. Sing and dance and be merry. Move the body. Don't we always feel better when we move and exercise?

Since school days, most people have been excited about dance nights. Music and movement together with other people. Whether around a fire, or at a nightclub, humans have moved and danced since the beginning of civilization.

Many people love to dance with others, but probably just as many are as happy to dance by themselves to a good rhythm.

It seems that moving is hard-wired in all of us. After all, our body is all movement. The heart is drumming. The blood is pulsing. The breath is waving. The nerves are pulsating. The cells are vibrating. The whole thing is just one big party of rhythms. No wonder we love to move. We have a deep need to move.

To feel happier, put a good rhythm on, and let your body move, jump-starting all the other rhythms and beats within.

Celebrate Life

I have a friend who sees the world with the eyes of a child. With beginner's mind. He gets incredibly excited about simple things. It's fun to be around him.

One day he calls me and declares: *We are having a fruit celebration! We have a watermelon, a pineapple, and other fruit and we are celebrating every piece of fruit as we eat it. Will you come and join us?*

Immediately, I found myself smiling at the simplicity of that. It is such a wonderful concept to celebrate life with our different actions, especially with food. It's very easy to appreciate good food.

That's what life is: a celebration. This whole universe is a celebration of existence. Every thing in the universe celebrates life in its own unique way. Why does a flower bloom? Why does it give fragrance? Why is it beautiful? The mind always asks this question. What is the reason for this, or for that?

Maybe at times it's just for fun, for joy, to celebrate life, its richness and multiplicity.

So I have started to celebrate life in different ways: in the food I eat, in the air I breathe, in the people I meet, and in the movements of my body. I've tried to celebrate the sun, the rain, the snow, a smile and a frown.

Let's try to celebrate life in a yoga class with movement and breath. Celebrate each breath by being mindful of every moment of the breathing process. You are breath. Can you believe how alive you can feel by just breathing!?

Celebrate being alive with every movement. Even as you open and close your hand. You can feel that you are part of this whole big thing we call life. Isn't that incredible? And you can feel so alive just by being mindful of every movement.

Good Vibes

If you listen to the news these days, it sure seems that the world is spinning out of balance, out of control, full of negative events, full of aggression and conflicts. Political debates, international conflicts, terrorism, poverty, brutality, environmental problems, and on and on.

It can be very depressing and seems hopeless. Many people feel that way. That means, as yogis, as conscious human beings, we have a job to do.

This world is an energetic scale. This universal scale always maintains balance. Energetically, the world cannot exist without balance.

For every light, there is a shadow. For every death, there is new life. For every loss, there is something to gain.

We do not understand beauty without also understanding ugliness. We do not know peace without having experienced confusion.

We do not seek happiness without first experiencing despair and suffering.

The balance of this world depends on you. As yogis, it is part of our work, our selfless gift, our mission, to create good in the world, to send out good vibes with our actions, words, and thoughts. The world needs you to do that to maintain the delicate balance, to counter-balance all we hear on the news.

This is a simple practice that makes the biggest difference. You can project a ripple of peace, love, and Light going out from your heart into the world.

Sitting quietly in a meditation posture (upright with back supported if necessary), repeat a simple mantra for two minutes each day:

Inhale – Peace Love & Light

Exhale – Peace Love & Light

As you breathe in, imagine that life force of the Universe carrying Peace and Love, flows into your heart center, lighting an Inner Light that shines brighter and brighter with every breath, like fire glowing brighter as it is fanned by the wind.

As you breathe out, imagine that your Inner Light radiates outward in all directions. Imagine these words and intentions rippling out into the collective consciousness and touching the hearts and minds of people all around the world.

The Driver

I stopped at a light. I could hear music coming from the car to my right as my windows were down. I looked over and saw a bright yellow convertible and a man with a huge smile, nodding his head to the beat of the music. He was looking straight at me. I smiled too.

Then, he lowered the volume and yelled out to me:

"You have a great smile! ... I wish you all the health and happiness in the world! ... And to your family! I hope you make a lot of money this year ..."

My lane was turning left and the light went green. The man didn't stop talking and saying praises. I had to go and couldn't say a word, just a *'Thank you, you too.'* I felt so overwhelmed with a flush of positive energy. The man was completely sincere.

As I drove away, I could see that he went back to listening to his music, and I could tell that at the next light, he was probably going to do the same thing to someone else.

Smiling at Strangers

Have you ever greeted a passerby, a total stranger on the street, with a friendly smile? Only to get back a blank stare, or a frown.

How did that make you feel?

If you are like most people, your mind probably protested the mini-injustice. *I just smiled at that guy! That .... (expletive)! Couldn't he just return the kind gesture?*

The mind wants to feel recognized when it does something good. But in yoga, such kind actions must be done with a selfless attitude. Expect nothing in return. Just create the good vibe.

The truth is, your kind smile made a difference. Have you ever walked down the street when a total stranger greeted you with a kind smile? Perhaps, you were too caught up in your thoughts to return it. But how did it make you feel? Chances are, you felt better. If you noticed it, you may have acknowledged it to yourself "that was a kind person" or "it's a good day today, people are smiling." It made a small yet significant impact on you.

Likewise, your kind smile made an impact on that un-smiling stranger. Next time, keep smiling, and don't let the mind get into that ego-talk of getting something in return. A smile is a gesture of selflessness that requires nothing in return.

Woofstock Festival:
The Sense of Joy

The week before Earth Day, in Balboa Park in San Diego, there is a festival for dogs. It's called the Woofstock Festival. It's a lot of fun for people, but especially fun for hundreds of dogs. They have different agility tests, loops, hurdles, and water puddles.

One thing I noticed at the festival was a loving atmosphere. I looked around at people and noticed that everyone was smiling, laughing, and having a good time. The dogs were having a blast. They were so in the moment. I was amazed at how focused the dogs were. They remained completely in the moment as they bounded around and sped through their routines. It reminded me of professional athletes who practice their skills over and over to perfection. Except the dogs just did it without much practice. Just due to their sense of joy and intense focus. In yoga and in meditation, we strive to develop this kind of focus. Perfectly in the moment, undisturbed. I thought, here is something we can learn from the dogs.

Another thing I noticed was complete lack of judgment on the dogs' part. They didn't look around to see how other dogs were stretching or running. They just did it. In a yoga class, we tend to compare and judge ourselves and others. We may think *"Oh, her ankles aren't aligned correctly, she is hurting herself, the teacher should say something to her"*, or *"that's gonna hurt, that's gonna cause some back pain if he keeps doing it like that"*, or *"I used to be able to reach my toes just a few years ago, so I gotta do it now."* That's normal. Our mind is conditioned to compare and analyze. But it takes us away from this moment. So this is another lesson we can learn from the dogs: to be in the moment, to not judge, to have fun, to be true to your self and your body's wisdom. If a dog missed a Frisbee, she didn't stop to say *"I wish I was a little faster,"* she just kept running and playing in the moment.

Let's try to be a little more like the dogs. Have fun. Look for the sense of joy in every movement. Those of us fortunate to be able to feel our bodies move and stretch should not take these sensory experiences for granted.

In a yoga class, perform the poses the way that is most natural for you. Remind yourself to come back to the moment. Catch your mind wandering, when it's judging, competing, or criticizing, and use those instances as triggers to come back to the Now.

RELATIONSHIPS, EMOTIONS, LOVE
Sri Lakshmi and
Importance of Friends

How do you tell if you are progressing in Yoga? Krishnamacharya, a great Yoga Master of the 20th century, suggests that your relationships will improve. You will be more kind, tolerant, accepting and forgiving, and more compassionate. You won't get into petty arguments with the people closest to you.

Our relationships play a big role in our mental health. One of the main reasons we need a complex mind is to interact with others. Healthy relationships directly affect your peace of mind. Many yogis tell us to seek out the company of spiritually elevating people, people who make you feel good and encourage you to grow. They call a company of such awesome people a *"Sangha"*, or a spiritual community.

I was once on a northbound train in India leaving Kerala and heading to Coimbatore, sitting and reading a book. An Indian girl, around ten years old, approached me out of the blue, stood three feet away from me, and stared.

That is not uncommon in India being one of very few Westerners traveling by myself, so I just smiled at her and kept reading. After a minute, and without introductions, she asked: *"What are you reading?"* I showed her my book. She asked again: *"What's your name?"* I introduced myself as Surya, my spiritual name, a name she would recognize as part of her culture, and in return asked her name. She said: *"My name is Sri Lakshmi."*

Then she proceeded to question me about where I was going, and what I was doing. She spoke excellent English. I told her that I was going back to Coimbatore to my teacher's ashram, and that I was a yoga teacher, and now exploring India as I had a little bit of time.

I asked her where she was traveling to, and she answered very sadly that she was coming back home.

"From where?"

She replied with a smile: *"I was in Dubai."*

"Wow! Dubai... that's far away isn't it?" She nodded and smiled.

"How do you like it there in Dubai?"

Her whole face lit up: *"I love it there! It's my most favorite place in the world."*

"Why?"

"Because I have friends there," she stated confidently.

We continued the conversation on the train for a while, and exchanged emails. Her parents sat across the aisle and smiled at their daughter's inquisitiveness.

Healthy friendships and relationships are where your heart is.

Surround yourself with good friends, like-minded people who share your interests and passion, and you'll find it much easier to stay grounded and keep your peace of mind.

Celestial Friends:
Yoga of the Heart

In India, when people talk about yoga practice, they often mean Prayer. It is a cultural custom to pray to multiple representations of the Divine Force: Shiva, Shakti, Krishna, Ganesh, Lakshmi, Hanuman, and many others.

Each deity represents a specific aspect of the Divine. Yet, all of them are part of the same Universal Consciousness. The Hindus assign different responsibilities to different deities. That way, it is easier to have a specific prayer, or conversation, with each of them. It is such a common practice in many Indian homes that people grow up praying, conversing with, and honoring their chosen deity. They hold simple and elaborate rituals for Hanuman, or Shiva, or any other deity they choose to honor.

They may ask Ganesh to remove obstacles on their life's path. They ask Lakshmi to be kind and provide abundance; Hanuman – to do a challenging task akin to moving a mountain, Krishna – to purify their ego and surrender their selfish thoughts.

What happens to an individual engaged in this type of conversation with divine helpers?

They build a relationship. Over time, as they reinforce these relationships through practice, i.e. prayer, they become habitual and part of one's world. It is as if one has a board of trusted advisors who can be called upon at any time anywhere. You can ask for advice, for help, for resolution, for freedom, for peace, for salvation. And you can share the burden of responsibilities with celestial beings, so you can relax and trust that they will take care of your problems while you sleep.

People who pray this way are more at peace, less stressed out, and more spiritual. They know that there is a divine hand in everything. They smile when things don't go as planned because they know that perhaps Shakti is getting involved to guide them on the right path.

Developing such relationships takes time. This practice is known as Bhakti Yoga, or Yoga of the Heart, because it is heart-opening to pray, to surrender selfish actions, and to bow to a greater force.

For Western minds, we may not feel a connection to Hindu deities. Any representation of the mystical Intelligence works. Mother Nature. Universal Self. Cosmic Consciousness. The key is to start the practice and make it a habit.

Gratitude in Action

Yoga practice is Gratitude in Action. I call it the "Able-Body Gratitude." We are able to move our bodies in ways that many people cannot. We are able to feel the sensations of stretching, toning, breathing, blood flow, and energy flow that are all miracles of nature.

As we practice physically, we can awaken the sense of gratitude for every movement we make.

Gratitude is a habit. It's one of the most life-transforming habits a person can develop.

Usually, we feel grateful for something when we are hit with the realization that we may lose it, like a loved one, or our health. We feel grateful for being healthy when we recover from disease. We feel grateful for having our family and friends around us when someone close to us passes away. Even the sudden realization of the possibility of losing someone dear may cause us to experience deep gratitude.

Deep Gratitude cuts through the fog of daily tasks and errands and forces us to take a sober look at the most important parts of our life.

Deep Gratitude grants us a sense of abundance. We acknowledge that we still have what we are grateful for. We are grateful for our health, for our loving relationships, for our work, and our ability to work.

How does one feel Deep Gratitude? Through prayer: a

heartfelt communion with a Greater Power. Prayer connects us to the greater Universal Power. We surrender our ego when we pray.

Gratitude is a prayer of thankfulness.

"Thank you, (God, Mother Nature, Divine Intelligence), for healing my body, for guiding me on the right path, for giving me strength, for supporting me in these challenging times, for giving me a loving family, for bringing the most wonderful person into my life, for providing me with an amazing opportunity, and so on..."

The main thing is, we will feel abundance through Gratitude, and the surrender of our ego, and a heartfelt connection to the Divine Force, when we make it a daily habit.

Imagine waking up every morning and feeling grateful for the day, for being alive, for being able to love and to work. That is a yogic practice of gratitude. It's none other than "counting your blessings" and seeing "the silver lining" in every situation. There is always something to be grateful for.

Thich Nhat Hanh,[14] a renowned Vietnamese Buddhist teacher calls it the "no-toothache gratitude: Isn't it great that you don't have a toothache right now?"

Some people keep a Gratitude Journal with which they start or end their day. I've seen people create a "Tree of Gratitude," a paper tree on a wall, where one can place paper leaves, one per day, each with something they are grateful for. Daily practice of gratitude forms a habit of feeling grateful, abundant, and happy.

Rhythms of Love

I remember a gathering of yogis who came together to chant some peaceful songs. The lead singer was a renowned artist. When he started, he closed his eyes and stayed silent for a few moments. His face reflected deep concentration and a faint smile as though he was gazing at something he adored. Then he started to chant. His voice carried an expression of total love and surrender toward the Divine Mother that he dedicated his chants for. He transmitted a feeling so deep and touching that he almost seemed to weep through his voice about his innermost pain and unconditional love.

Kirtan, devotional chanting, is one of *Bhakti* yoga practices. When lead by skillful musicians able to convey real love through their voice, it is heart-opening and transformative. I especially find Kirtans transforming when attended by many people. The voices of many people chanting all at once create waves of energy, vibrations of peace and love that affect everyone nearby. When experienced in a group setting, it can be incredibly moving.

In every major city, there are Kirtan groups these days. If you want to feel your heart pulse with rhythms of love, attend one of them.

Emotions as Tools

My wife, Theresa, told me about a pair of rabbits at an animal shelter who were bonded for life. They shared their enclosure and cared for each other, grooming, sharing food, and sleeping side by side.

Time came for one of the rabbits to pass on. Once she was gone, and the staff took her body away, the other rabbit searched around the enclosure for several hours, sniffing the corners, the food, the bedding. He stopped eating for the day and kept fussing around.

The next day, he was back to his routine as normal. One can argue that he forgot. But he didn't. He just moved on. He grieved for the day, and the next day he moved on to the present.

Emotions can overwhelm and overpower us. Sometimes we wear our emotions on our sleeve, as the saying goes, - we represent our emotions. Emotions become us. This is not always a good thing.

In yoga, we learn to dis-identify from our emotions as much as we learn to dis-identify from our body-mind. Mainly, we learn to observe our emotions in the same way as we observe our breath or our thoughts. This way we gain control of our emotions by being their witness. We can still allow our emotions to flow through and influence us, but we do it consciously with control rather than plunging deep into an emotional chasm without any regard for our actions.

The rabbit in the story took his time to grieve, then left his grief where it belonged – in the past, and moved on. People have a harder time doing that. Our mind drifts into the past all the time. While it is natural to contemplate on past events and actions, it is not always helpful with moving forward in our lives.

In those circumstances, when one needs to move on, it is very helpful to keep this in mind: Happiness depends on two things: personal growth and contribution to others. Both of these aspects of our life: personal growth and contribution happen in the present moment. Therefore they take us away from dwelling in the past and spiraling into an emotional mess. Furthermore, growth and contribution make one feel the sense of moving forward, of accomplishment, of making a difference, and ultimately, of happiness.

There is however a possibility of a powerful emotion such as grief or anger or depression that may completely overpower us for a period of time. As long as it's not harmful to yourself and others around, it is important to give it time to move through you. You may even imagine the emotion as a wave rolling through your being and eventually subsiding.

When you notice yourself in the middle of it, you will need to create a habit of interruption. This means that you need to have an automatic response to separate yourself from the emotion and become its witness. Instead of being consumed by and identifying with the emotional torrent, you interrupt its overpowering effect and simply witness it. See it as a tool. What can you learn from it? Emotions are great teachers.

Yoga provides some wonderful tools to interrupt the emotional hurricane.

The most common tool is the breath. Taking deep slow breaths is a great interruptor of emotions. It keeps you in the moment and takes your mind away from the emotion and focuses it on the deep breathing.

Another interruptor is the use of sound. Sounding OM, for example, or expressing how you feel through a sound like "Haaaa!" will accomplish the same goal – take your attention away from the consuming emotion. Of course, you will need to be in a publicly acceptable space to yell out at the top of your lungs.

If you have a meditation technique, you may use it to interrupt the emotion as well. The use of peaceful images, inspiring people (teachers like Gandhi or Mother Teresa), visualization of positive energy and chakras (energy centers) – all fall into the category of appropriate tools.

Whatever tool you use, the most important aspect is to make it a habitual response. As you feel anger, or sadness, sorrow, or despair, find a trigger to unleash the interruptor response. Begin the breath. Chant OM. Visualize. After a few seconds of focusing on your tool, you become a witness to your emotion. Then, you can say: "What is good about this? What can I learn from this emotion? Let me watch it. Let me stay here without running away from it, denying it, or identifying with it. Let me observe its effect on my body and mind." After a while, you will be ready to process it and leave it where it belongs – in the past.

Car Service

After a yoga class, a student went to pick up his car from car service. He drove away and within minutes his car broke down. Confused, he tried to restart it in vain. Feeling a little angry, he remembered the yoga class: emotions are tools. He decided to watch his anger, and not act on it. He breathed deeply while sitting in his car for a few minutes.

After a minute, he calmly called the car service and explained what happened. They came to pick it up. He smiled and patiently waited observing his emotions and reactions.

Once the car was fixed, the service personnel came out and said: *"You've been so calm and polite. This is all free of charge and we will refund your original charges, too. Thank you for being so patient!"*

Archie and Loving Attitude:
Yoga of Emotions

There's a neighborhood cat around where we live. We call him Archie. He is a very friendly fluffy ball of fur and loves to be petted. Every time I am outside to practice yoga, he comes by, rubs against my legs, and flops over on his back expecting a massage.

A few weeks ago, as usual, I was petting Archie, when all of a sudden, he turned around, grabbed my hand with his claws and teeth, and went totally crazy for a few seconds. He scratched up my hand pretty badly. And then he jumped away, 'smiled', and walked off like nothing happened. I totally didn't expect that.

In the first few seconds that followed, I watched myself being angry at the cat. Even a couple of minutes later, as I was trying to stop the bleeding, I was still upset. I had a thought: How can I be upset at an innocent creature that reacts according to his instincts? But the ego-part of my mind was still very angry at Archie. I reminded myself to observe these feelings in me, with patience and curiosity.

I remembered the story that Swami Satchidananda told in one of his weekly Yoga lectures at Satchidananda Ashram – Yogaville in Virginia, about a swami who claimed he conquered the emotion of anger.

This swami went away into the mountains for many years. He stayed in a cave far away from people. He meditated and felt that he attained a certain degree of enlightenment.

He came back into his village, and the word spread that the enlightened swami was back from his retreat. Villagers came to see him and to ask him about his experience.

Swami sat in a Lotus posture under a banyan tree, serenely regarding his audience, and answered questions.

One villager asked: "Sir, when you were up there by yourself all this time, was there any moment that you felt angry?"

"Why? I did not. I observed my emotions and conquered them."

"Yes, sir, but was there any moment at all that you felt angry?" The villager insisted.

"No. As I said, I conquered my emotions, including anger." The swami stared at the inquirer getting annoyed at his persistence. "I understand, sir, but please think hard, maybe for a fleeting moment, you might have felt a little bit of anger?"

The swami got up and roared at the questioner: "I already told you I completely conquered anger!"

The story illustrates that being in control of the emotions and feeling spiritual is easy when being by yourself, away from everyone else. As soon as we start dealing with other people and different temperaments, we get tested.

This story also shows indirectly that emotions can be tools. Anger can be used as a tool to serve a good purpose if one is in control of it. To develop such control, we first need to be able to observe it with dispassion, without becoming anger.

Right after the incident with "Archie the cat", I tried to do just that. I tried to observe what anger felt like. At first, I noticed that I was able to observe it in a way we could observe hot or cold. Then, the longer I watched it, the less I felt it. It became much more of a concept in my mind than an actual physical emotion I felt in my body.

The next morning, I was sitting for meditation and started off with cultivating a loving attitude. That's a practice I like to do once in a while – to regard the whole of nature with a loving attitude. Whatever comes into your awareness, whether from inside of your own body or from the outside, consider it with a loving attitude. This includes irritating sounds, uncomfortable physical sensations, uncomfortable feelings, and annoying thoughts. All of a sudden, the image of Archie popped into my mind. I smiled and, like any other image, I watched it with loving attention. I also searched for any feelings of anger left inside with the same loving attention. But there was no anger left.

Take a moment to do this practice. Consider everything within your current awareness with loving and kind attention: the body, the breath, the trees outside, the sky, the people, and so on.

Love is All We Need

I was driving recently and noticed very rude drivers (Boston is infamous for them). They cut others off, didn't wait for their turn, honked in annoyance, and tailgated. I wondered to myself 'why are some people so impatient and mean? Is it their nature? Are some people naturally mean?'

Then someone cut me off. After a few minutes, another driver didn't let me go when it was my turn. I could feel a slight agitation within myself. And then, I realized that if this goes on, without being mindful of my feelings and breathing out all the mental negativity, I would probably turn into one of those mean drivers, too.

I also realized that these people may be caught up in a mental game of getting back at others for being treated unkindly in the first place. They may see themselves as victims to whom life has been unfair, so they feel hurt and angry. Maybe they simply didn't get enough love that day, or maybe they didn't get enough love in their lives. Perhaps, they grew up without much love and care. It wasn't even their fault. Instead, they experienced neglect and other negative emotions around them or directed at them. And now, of course, their actions may be subconscious, not intentional.

I realized that there's a cycle of being mean to each other. What has to happen to stop the cycle?

Maybe, a smile. Simple and sincere. A gesture of kindness. A kind word. This has to be done in spite of the negativity. That is the challenge. This is where we can learn to use our internal spiritual strength. Only then can people receive the love they need and start healing and awakening, and treating others in a kind way.

This concept has a name: the Principle of Reciprocity. We tend to treat others they way we are treated. We mimic and conform to the behaviors of those around us. If a person is kind to you, you tend to be kind back. If a driver cuts you off, you tend to get angry, too.

To not-conform to this principle and break the cycle, we must identify this tendency first. As soon as you become aware that you are being treated a certain way, and notice your reaction to reciprocate the same way, pause and consciously choose your reaction. Can I influence the situation in a positive way? Can I turn the tide? Simply by using my inner strength to control my reactions.

Love is All Around Us

Hugh Grant says in the movie "Love Actually" that *"Love is actually all around us."* Isn't that the truth!

Everything loves in nature. Birds love to sing. Flowers love to bloom. Snails love to eat plants. Skunks love to eat snails. Crows love to be mischievous.

In our bodies, everything loves, too. Muscles love to stretch, move, and tone. Lungs love to open fully with breath. Every cell loves to receive oxygen and be nourished.

If every cell of the body loves, we are all pure Love.

Mind loves to think and analyze. Ego loves to feel important. Inner Self loves to shine through like the Sun through the clouds.

Indeed, some things are not Love. But why focus on it? When there is so much Love all around. Plus, this is a way of looking at the world to see Love and create Love all around. This is a tool – to see Love in all of your actions, in all of your movements, and in others.

Starting with asana practice, notice how your back loves to lengthen, the shoulders love to relax, the breath loves to flow.

The Onion

Three yogis decide to climb a mountain. A Hatha yogi (specializing in physical yoga poses) commits to the arduous task, climbing slowly, resting as needed, rock by rock, ledge by ledge, until he eventually reaches the summit many days later.

A Bhakti yogi (specializing in Yoga of the Heart) prays to Krishna, the Divine Lord. As he prays, he recognizes the nature of the mountain is divine. It is a representation of Divine Mother. "Please let me dissolve into your Love." He finds himself on the summit.

A Jnana yogi (a yogi of self-inquiry and wisdom) sits down to meditate on the mountain and realizes that there is no difference between his own Self and the mountain, that all is One, and he instantly finds himself at the summit.

There is a practice in Jnana Yoga called Neti Neti (not this not that) which involves a careful reflection into our deepest nature. What is at the core of our being? Much like peeling the skins of an onion, the practitioner discards different attributes that we use to describe ourselves and identify with.

"I am not my occupation…

"I am not this physical body… or this sensation in my back .. or this sensation in my stomach .. What is beyond the body?

"I am not my flowing breath … What gives rise to the breath?

"I am not the mind .. not this particular thought .. or this specific distraction … what is deeper and beyond the mind?

"I am not my emotions…

"I am not my relationships…

"I am not the witness that observes all these attributes. What is deeper and beyond the witness?"

Eventually, the practitioner ends up with Silence and Pure Awareness. The mind is not able to identify with what is truly beyond the mind's reaches. Pure Awareness is the state of True Self.

When the onion's layers have been peeled off, we discover that there is no core, or center. There is in fact Nothing.

What makes the room that you are sitting in? Is it the four walls? Take away the walls, the space is still the same, but the room is gone.

Our body is the same as the room. The body houses the Spirit, or Consciousness. Without the body, Consciousness is unmanifested, but like the space without walls, it is still here, and everywhere.

Physical attributes like the physical body gives Consciousness a way to be manifested. Yet, the nature of Consciousness is Absolute. Our True Nature is Absolute, and is not limited to this body. It is only housed in this body for the time being. When the walls are removed, or the body passes away, the Consciousness remains.

A Jnana yogi meditates on the nature of Consciousness and peels the layers of the Onion.

PART 4:
Stories, Meditations, Poems

*"Children who do not hear stories when they're young experience
a developmental stunting, and permanently lose the ability to
visualize, imagine, and, to a large extent, empathize."*
(Thom Hartmann)[15]

Stories, Meditations, Poems

Nature provides inspiration to people in every culture. In Siberia, nature is everywhere. It surrounds large cities and swallows small towns. There are no suburbs once the city limits are left behind. Thick hundred-year-old forests of pine, aspen, and birch trees form an endless sea of green colors around all livable places. From an airplane, the villages and houses are lonely islands with miles and miles of forest in between. When flying over Siberia at night, you do not see signs of human influence very much or the typical flashing lights down below from towers or houses. Instead, down below is pitch black. For hours and hours. One can appreciate the vastness and remoteness of this land from an airplane.

Several times I had the opportunity to fly in a helicopter over this Siberian landscape with a family friend. The first time, six or seven of us prepared food for a picnic and flew for a couple of hours out of town in the northeastern direction with no particular destination in mind. It was a bright sunny day in late summer. The pilot told us that he would land the helicopter on a flat meadow somewhere far away. Sure enough, in a couple of hours, we hovered over an open plateau on top of a high mountain range, slowly descending. From above, as far as our eyes could see, hundreds of round mirror-like lakes reflected the sun and altogether formed a giant tapestry of lights.

"Has anyone ever seen this place?" one of us asked. The pilot shook his head, *"I doubt it, there is no way to get here other than a helicopter. We are probably the very first humans witnessing this place and stepping down on this ground."*

We walked around for hours, awestruck and enchanted by this corner of the world, gathering berries and filling our flasks with the clearest water from the tiny lakes. As we sat down to eat our lunch, a herd of deer came by our camp and stared at us for a while, curious and unafraid. *"There are plenty of brown bears here, too,"* the pilot warned. But we did not see one that day.

I never went back to that spot again. The pilot could not seem to find it on our subsequent trips. There was also an unspoken understanding in everyone from the first trip that we had all visited a magical land. Returning there may ruin the memory of our first experience. We flew in different directions every time, landing in open valleys, mountain ranges, and next to giant lakesides. We did spot brown bears as well as wolves, lynx, and moose on other trips.

The following is a collection of writings that reflect the poetic elements of nature and underlie the metaphors for life and for our minds.

Five Elements of Nature

Give thanks to the highest teacher. Many, if not all, of our insights are inspired by Mother Nature. As it states in an old yogic text, "The Mother is a passionate dancer behind All." What can we learn from Her?

As you prepare to meditate, acknowledge Her with gratitude.

Earth. Feel the support of the Earth beneath your body. Notice how grounded you feel. The Earth is always there to support you even when you may feel no other support in your life.

Fire. Feel the warmth inside your body; the heartbeat pulsing warmth and energy. Allow vibrant health and warmth to radiate from your heart.

Water. Feel the power of water in your body: powerful and fluid, supple and graceful.

Air. Feel the freedom and ease of Air flowing in and out; the lungs expanding and contracting like a wave.

Ether. Observe the space beyond your thoughts. Feel the wholeness of existence without attachment to anything physical or mental. If your thoughts were clouds in the sky, what is the Sky?

Mother Nature is a profound teacher offering countless insights.

Meditate on Her five elements with a bow of gratitude.

In Siberia

A few years ago, my wife and I were sitting on a high cliff looking over one of the world's largest rivers, the Yenisey. It runs through my home city of Krasnoyarsk in Siberia and, over the ages, has carved deep and beautiful canyons on both sides.

Our cliff is about thirty miles up the river, south of the city. We can see five or six miles out, maybe more, if it wasn't for the distant haze coming from the smoke of chimneys in the village below.

Here, at this particular point, another river called Mana flows into the Yenisey, creating a wide delta. Natural beauty is so stunning that for the first few moments upon seeing it one is left without words.

I have to remind myself to breathe. The air is very clean, so we sit down quietly and breathe deeply for a while. There are impressive mountains with ancient forests all around the river delta.

We notice several hawks circling around, riding the warm air, and trilling to each other. My wife counts nine of them.

Our cliff sits so high that we are looking down at the hawks soaring and spiraling over the water.

I begin to follow one of the birds with my eyes. It rarely flaps its wings. Its connection with its environment, the air current, is perfect. The control of its body is flawless. Each minutest movement of the wing is intentional and in the moment. I wonder to myself: Could the hawk be practicing yoga? Could it be in meditation?

I continue to watch it for a long time, riding the air currents, circling, over the water, and over the trees. The sun dips its lower edge behind the far-away mountain silhouettes.

I draw my attention away from the hawk. My mind is very calm. I thank the hawk mentally for sharing its meditation with me.

It's time to go to make a light dinner, and prepare Banya (traditional sauna).

Heaven and Hell

(This story has been told in spiritual circles of various traditions
for many generations and I never discovered its real origin)

Aholy man was having a conversation with the Lord one
day and said.
"Lord, I would like to know what Heaven and Hell are like."
The Lord led the holy man to two doors. He opened one
of the doors and the holy man looked in. In the middle of
the room was a large round table. In the middle of the table
was a large pot of stew, which smelled delicious and made
the holy man's mouth water.

The people sitting around the table were thin and sickly.
They appeared to be famished. They were holding spoons
with very long handles that were strapped to their arms and
each found it possible to reach into the pot of stew and take a
spoonful. But because the handle was longer than their arms,
they could not get the spoons back into their mouths.

The holy man shuddered at the sight of their misery
and suffering.

The Lord said, *"You have seen Hell."*

They went to the next room and opened the door. It was
exactly the same as the first one. There was the large round
table with the large pot of stew which made the holy man's
mouth water.

The people were equipped with the same long-handled spoons strapped to their arms, but here the people were well nourished and happy, laughing and talking.

The holy man said, *"I don't understand."*

"It is simple," said the Lord. *"It requires but one skill. You see they have learned to feed each other, while the greedy think only of themselves."*

A Curly Hair

*(a story from a lecture by Yoga Master Swami Satchidananda
at Satchidananda Ashram – Yogaville in Virginia.)*

Once upon a time, a man asked a yogi to grant him a personal genie so that he can have the genie do whatever he wishes. The yogi agreed but warned the man that the genie must have something to do or he will eat the man.

"Oh, not a problem," the man said, *"I have plenty of tasks for him."* As soon as the genie appeared, he asked for work. So the man commanded him to build a beautiful palace full of furniture, thinking that it will take the genie some time. But to his surprise, the genie was done in seconds.

The man asked for servants. Snap! In a fraction of a second, the palace was full of servants. The man asked for food. Snap! Tables full of all kinds of food imaginable appeared right in front of him.

Soon, the man had nothing to ask for. The genie turned on him ready to eat him. The man got frightened and ran back to the yogi, with the genie following close behind.

"Please," he begged the yogi, *"Could you take him away! I can't find any more things for him to do. I am sorry that I was so selfish."* The yogi took pity: *"OK. I'll take care of the genie."* He plucked a curly hair from his head and handed it to the

genie: "*Here, straighten this hair and stand it on its end.*"

The genie pulled the hair straight but as soon as he let it go, the curly hair curled back into a spiral. Again and again, the genie tried, but how could he straighten a really curly hair!

Then, the yogi addressed the man: "*Whenever you have something for the genie to do, ask him to do it. As soon as he is done, ask him to go back to the curly hair.*"

In this story, the genie represents the mind, powerful, obsessive, and self-destructive. The curly hair is a meditation practice like mantra repetition, a positive thought, or breathing focus. Whenever your mind does not have to be occupied, why allow it to drive you crazy? Give the mind a curly hair to work with – let it focus on a meditation practice – and you'll always retain your peace.

How We Find Energy

When you feel tired, when your Prana (life force) is low, what do you do? I asked this question in class. Here are the responses I received.

- We find energy in food, by having hunger and appetite for food, and in hunger and appetite for life,
- In laughter and in smiles,
- By having a passion,
- In creative tasks,
- Through motivation and inspiration,
- In relationships with people and with children,
- By being part of a community,
- By drinking fresh juice and good coffee and lots of water,
- By fasting and cleansing,
- By having a positive attitude,
- In love and compassion,
- When the mind is quiet, and by being present,
- In meditation, movement and exercise, and weight lifting,
- In the practice of yoga asanas, especially inversions, backbends, and sun salutations, and
- Through the breath, and
- Being in nature, breathing fresh air, by the ocean, and in the mountains,
- By getting the sunshine,
- Hiking, running, swimming, and biking,

- Listening to music, and by making music,
- While 'stepping back' and goal-setting,
- While bathing,
- When dancing,
- By generating ideas,
- Teaching,
- Having a purpose,
- Sleeping,
- Traveling and having adventures,
- By making new friends,
- Singing, chanting, and Oming,
- Through touch, hugging, massage, and making love,
- And smelling aromatherapy, and
- By just having fun,
- Painting, cooking, and knitting,
- By spending time in solitude,
- Learning and philosophizing,
- Reading, writing and journaling, and
- Making a life or bucket list, and
- In prayer, and
- Being with animals,
- By 'being done,' and
- Through gratitude.

Lines in the Sand

What is a border between two countries, or two houses, but a 'line in the sand?'

Two young boys are playing on the beach, digging up holes in the sand, sifting through the sand for any seashell treasures.

One boy draws a line in the sand and says that he will dig on the one side of the line and his friend on the other.

As they play on their separate sides, each boy looks over to see what the other boy has in their collection of shells. The grass is always greener on the other side.

One boy spots a really pretty shell in his friend's collection, and asks if he can have it in exchange for three of his best-looking shells. Isn't that much like a trade exchange between two countries?

Begrudgingly, the other boy agrees. He gives up his treasure but harbors some attachment to it. When his friend is not looking, he quickly crosses the line in the sand and 'steals' the shiny shell. Hiding it in the sand, he pretends like nothing happened. Isnt' that much like spying and stealing between two countries, businesses, or any other neighbors?

However, the other boy notices that his prized possession is gone. He searches for it everywhere on his side of the line, very upset. And then, he suspects that the 'crime' may have taken place. He notices the footprints in the sand, and questions his friend on the other side.

His friend pretends that he knows nothing about it. But the footprints give him away. The boy calls his friend a thief and traitor and tries to cross over the line to search for his treasure. The 'thief' springs up into action and blocks his way, pushing his friend of five minutes past back into his territory. A war ensues. Isn't that much like a conflict between any two countries and neighbors?

Neither of the boys really own their sand plots, or the tiny treasure. The ownership of land, or things, is just an illusion.

Is that not so in the adult world?

What is a border but a line in the sand?

Who is the true owner of treasures but the Earth itself?

We claim ownership of things that never belonged to us.

From a yogi's perspective, the concept of worldly possessions is odd. You may 'take care' of a few things in your lifetime, but always keep in mind that you only borrow them from Mother Earth, and will return them to Her when it's time.

What Matters

I thought today: What if I died tomorrow?
Have you ever had that thought?
Have you said everything you want to say to the people you love?
How have you treated the people who love you up until now?
What would you do today if you knew?
What actions would you take right now?
Would you serve others? Would you be selfish?
What legacy would you leave if you died tomorrow?
What are you doing every day to live a life with no regrets?
What do you love?
What are you doing now to show your love? To show you are alive?
Are you doing things that really matter?
Are you living in the present?

Silk Moth

Our life is like the lifecycle of a silk moth.

- **We are either eating** – taking without giving
- **Getting entangled** – with material possessions, and obligations
- **Locked up in a cocoon** – suffocating, bloated, and starting to look inward
- **Transforming** – meditating, yearning for freedom, and starting to get rid of old destructive bonds and attachments
- **Or growing wings** – realizing our True Nature

Where are you in the process?

Pants On Fire

What would you do if, right now, your pants were on fire? Fully ablaze, scorching hot. Would you ignore it? Would you be distracted with social media, the news, or your iPhone?

Probably not. I bet you would not worry about anything else but putting out the flames. You would not worry about your makeup or hair, or your dinner plans, or the emails you received. Your full attention would be on the fire. You would jump into cold water, strip the pants down even if someone was watching, and scream as if your life depended on it.

Your life depends on putting out such a flame. The ego conspires in most obnoxious and subtle ways to deceive you on your path to the True Self. Like putting out the fire, it is of greatest importance to not fall prey to the ego. Will you find Ultimate Peace and Happiness in this life? Only if it is as important as putting out that fire.

Smells Like Life

A small group of young kids tiptoed through the woods. They barely made any noise, each pretending to be their favorite animal. Predator or prey, each had to be acutely observant and mindful of their surroundings, carefully placing their feet as they moved forward. The teacher marveled at the kids' innate sense of connection.

Minutes later, the group came to a small marshy pond within the forest exploring the multitude of detail. A five-year old girl dug her hands into the soft ground and produced a handful of leaves, moss, and soil. She smelled it with the air of an expert botanist.

The teacher asked: *"What does it smell like?"*

The girl paused and smiled, announcing simply: *"It smells like life."*

"Wow, I didn't know what life smelled like."

"Yep, this is it," she declared. *"It smells just like Life."*

Unity

I was sitting in the backyard as a beautiful spring day in New England was winding down.

The sun was setting slowly. Birds were busy in preparation for the night. Warm gentle wind played with tree leaves.

My meditative focus kept getting lost in random thoughts.

I noticed that the tree leaves sparkled in the sun. The leaves reflected the slanted sunrays like tiny mirrors. Each leaf shimmered with the silver and golden light of the sun, and rocked gently on its stem, cradled by the wind. The tree as a whole was covered in silvery golden brilliance. It pulsed with energy.

I became the tree for a few moments.

Then, my mental self took over. My mind started to explain what I was witnessing. That's when I lost the connection. But it was enough to know that I am the tree, the birds, the sunrays, and the wind.

Courage

To be in the moment requires courage,
An adventure, a mystery, a leap of faith.
You do not know what awaits
When you cut the binding ties,
If you'll come out unscathed
From the unknown
When you burst open the doors of the labyrinth –
This mind that you own
Which conspires to trap your attention
Within its many walls
Seducing you with familiar comfort.
Why leave this cozy place?
Why go anywhere at all?
Even though it keeps you trapped and entangled,
Even the fears are familiar,
And the worries and the habits that annoy you and others,
Yet they too become yours and comfortable like old friends
Who tell you to stay back and forget about new dreams.
Stay here, be comfortable
The world out there is too wild
It may be dangerous
It's foolish to leave the confines of the mind
Don't be a child!
Despite the warnings, in spite of it all

You choose to leap forth
You pause but don't stall
And burst the doors open into the light
Cut free the needy tentacles
And discover what might
Be here …
What is this moment?
This moment …
Do you know what happens next?
A whisper
A knock
A grumbling
A ticking clock
Breath
Birdsong
Something new, unknown, fresh
Every moment all along
Then, like a fisherman waiting to cast his net
A flood of thoughts invades
And pulls you back into sinking forgetfulness.
Something within you stays alert and resolute
Sweeping the blazing torch of determination
Swinging the sharp blade of focus
You stay put
In the present
Like a warrior
Unyielding
Fire burning within

Eyes ablaze
Unconquerable.

Mind the Gap

Mind the Gap that exists after exhale ends
and before inhale begins.
Mind the fleeting thoughts.
Mind the Gap that exists when one thought fades into the
Subconscious and before another enters and attaches its sticky
uniqueness to the mental screen.
This in-between Gap is Infinity,
This present moment exists forever.
This Gap is a pause in your physical reality,
It is the entry point to Nirvana.
Nirvana is the Super-conscious state,
Where past and future are mental illusions.
When your mind gains clarity, it becomes a clean slate
Without worry, sadness, fear, or confusion.
But in fact, that Gap is the only thing that exists.
That Gap is the only thing that is real.
Even though our precious ego resists
To give up its reign, you still feel
Deep down, in your core, in your heart,
That this pause is what's real.
When the mind pauses,
You experience who you really are.

Wild Wind

Wild wind danced with the trees in the windows of my meditation room. I could hear it howling and attacking the roofs of houses. I could almost feel the wind as it made attempts to get into the cracks in the windowpanes.

I sat in my quiet posture with my mind like the wind, twirling from thought to thought.

"A busy, spinning mind is like a hurricane," I recalled a yoga teaching. The center of the hurricane is always still, and it's only the outside air that spins faster and faster.

I imagined myself sitting in the still center of the hurricane. It was easy – as the wind outside was believably hurricane-like. All of a sudden, the whirlwind weather became a useful tool to find Stillness.

The familiar dance between the Stillness and the mind ensued. As I lost my center, I would ask:

Where is the center of the hurricane?

Where is the center around which my thoughts are spinning?

Is there a still center behind and in-between my thoughts?

Where am I before the thoughts arise?

Who Moved My Yoga Mat!?

A: What's this?

B: Excuse me?

A: What's this?

B: What do you mean? This is a yoga mat.

A: Yes, I see that. It's MY yoga mat, but why is it over there?

B: Well, I didn't think it was anyone's mat, so I moved it over a little. You still have plenty of room.

A: Not really ... (sigh) ... that's just rude.

B: I'm sorry. ... Let's not make a big deal, please. We are at a yoga class.

A: Yeah, supposed to be respectful and mindful of others.

Ommmm

Ommmmm

Ommmmmm

(Seventy-five minutes later)

A: Sorry about the mat thing.

B: Oh, that's OK. I am sorry I moved it. ...

This was a great class, wasn't it?

A: Yes, great class. I feel so much better now.

B: Me too.

Dandelion Mind

I walked outside with a question: What would my mind look like in the outside world?

I looked around, feeling the air. Right in front of me, a sea of green rolled and danced with the breeze. The maple trees swayed their branches; their leaves fluttered in the wind. Everything was in constant motion. That is like my mind, I thought.

What would I prefer my mind to be like? I asked next.

Again, I scanned my view. Suddenly, a tall stalk of a single yellow dandelion flower caught my sight. It stood well above the ground, and swayed gently in the wind. It was strong, yet flexible, grounded in the earth, yet bold to reach out to the sky. I fixed my attention on the dandelion, feeling its rhythm, listening to its story.

That's what my mind would be like, I thought. I'd like to have a mind like a dandelion.

A Tree on Fire

It was a warm sunny morning after a snowstorm in New England. I looked over at a tree across the street. Its branches were covered with melting snow, but the snow was turning fast into water under the beaming sun.

The sun illuminated the tree. Its branches sparkled with every color of the rainbow. Dripping, reflecting light, the tree looked like it was on fire from the inside out. The reds, blues, greens, pinks, and orange colors were in continuous motion, flickering, shimmering, intensifying, and dissolving every second.

The sun rays came in at a slanted angle so that I could see them piercing through the tree. The tree loved the sun's attention. I think it was waking up from its winter dream with a brilliant smile.

The Play of Consciousness

Have you ever watched waves break against rocks and splash into thousands of crystalline pieces?

Have you listened to the sound of the rain drumming on the earth?

Have you watched strong playful wind toss the leaves of trees in every direction?

Have you sat still to notice the quiet in the air in the early morning before nature wakes up?

And as it wakes up, have you seen the first rays of sunlight shimmer off the leaves with sparkles?

What we see is none other than the Infinite at play. Mother Nature is in every moment of stillness and in every moment of movement.

Let Go of Agenda

Every morning I do my practice: yoga asanas, breathing, and meditation. For the meditation, I have a specific sequence that I like. It's a sequence of different concentration techniques, which gradually take me to a deeper and quieter place.

One morning, after I finished this routine and was about to end my practice, something happened … All of a sudden, a deep part of my being relaxed, and my whole body became completely still. I observed my breath slow down to an imperceptible rhythm. My mind seemed empty, open and aware. All of a sudden, I could see and feel everything. There was still the sense of "I," but it was very faint, only a light shadow of my ego.

After I came out of that, I realized: Once there is no more agenda, no more "have to accomplish something" (even if it's your meditation practice), it happens. Once you have a feeling that there is nothing that you have to do; once there is a feeling that you've already accomplished everything that you ever needed or wanted, the mind dissolves into Stillness.

This Moment

Remember the good old times?
When you lived by the ocean …
When you traveled in Europe …
When you listened to the sounds of crickets at night …
When you walked along the beach …
When you hiked up the mountains …
When you stood at the edge of a wild canyon to smell the eucalyptus trees and hear the buzzing of the hummingbirds
Remember that time when …
You first fell in love …
You jumped off rocks into the cold ocean water …
You drove into a snowstorm …
You left your parent's house for the last time as you moved away on your own …
You realized how rare true friendship really is …
The rain and the wind and even the snow didn't stop you from running outside …
Why were those moments so special?
Why do we remember them for the rest of our lives?

Is it, perhaps, because we were not thinking about the past when we lived those moments? We were fully in the present.

In fact, we don't remember the times that we sat and thought about the past. We only remember the times when we lived fully in the moment.

As the saying goes *"Life is not the days you have lived, but the days you remember."*

Live in the present, and this moment, too, will become special.

References & Reading Recommendations

1. *The Teachings of Don Juan* by Carlos Castaneda; the shaman Don Juan attempts to "awaken" the author from the everyday reality into the reality of the dreams.

2. *The Yoga Sutras of Patanjali: Translation and Commentary* by Sri Swami Satchidananda; www.integralyoga.org.

3. Lewis, P.J. (2006). *Stories I teach live by.* Qualitative Inquiry, 12(5), 829-849.

4. Story adopted from Robert Fulghum's writings from www.robertfulghum.com.

5. Berry, T. (2009). Thomas Berry. Adapted from www.thomasberry.org.

6. Alan Watts, Nature of Consciousness Lecture Series by Sounds True Audio Archives.

7. Paolo Coelho, *Like A River Flowing* and other writings.

8. Dan Millman, *The Way of the Peaceful Warrior.*

9. Carl Jung, *Psychology of the Unconscious* and other writings.

10. Lopez, B. (1990). *Crow and Weasel.* New York: North Point Press.

11. Jean Giono, French author of *The Man Who Planted Trees*, first published in 1953.

12. Henry David Thoreau, *Walking* – a lecture and an essay written between 1851 and 1860 during Thoreau's Walden years.

13. *Becoming the Iceman* by Wim Hof, 2011.

14. Thich Nhat Hanh, from one of his writings. His most famous book is *Peace is Every Step*.
15. Hartmann, Thom. (1998). *The Prophet's Way*. Park Street Press.

Glossary of Sanskrit Words and Phrases

Agnisar Dhauti Stomach cleansing technique

Ahamkara Ego

Ahimsa Non-violence

Aparigraha Non-hoarding, moderation

Asteya Non-stealing

Atman Soul, individual divine Self

Bhakti Surrender of ego through love/devotion

Bhavana Visualization

Bodhisattva Enlightened being/divine helper

Brahmacharya Celibacy/Faithfulness

Buddhi Discerning intellect, Higher mind

Dharana Concentration

Dhyana Meditation

Ganesh Elephant God, remover of obstacles

Hanuman Monkey God, makes impossible happen

Jivamukti Liberated, enlightened being

Jnana Yoga Yoga of self-inquiry, self-knowledge

Kapalabhati Skull-shining breath, breath of fire

Karma Law of action and reaction

Karma Yoga Selfless service, yoga of selfless action

Krishna Absolute Consciousness

Kumbhaka Breath retention

Lakshmi Goddess of abundance

Manas The five senses

Maya Illusion of physical reality, of permanence

Moksha Liberation, freedom from suffering

Namaste Greeting, *"I see my divine Self in you"*

Namaskar Greeting

Niyamas Principles of personal conduct

Prana Life force, energy

Pranayama Breathing exercises to build/control Prana

Pratipaksha Bhavana Substituting positive thoughts for negative ones, counting your blessings

Rishi Seer, enlightened sage

Sadhana Spiritual practice

Samadhi Self-Realization, Absorption in True Self

Samskara Deep-seated pattern, habitual behavior

Sangha Spiritual community

Santosha Contentment

Satya Truth/Truthfulness

Shakti Manifested reality/Divine feminine

Shiva Consciousness/Absolute reality/Divine masculine

Swami A renunciate, Hindu monk

Tapas/Tapasya Burning (of ego), self-discipline

Uddhyana Bandha Stomach lift exercise

Vairagya Non-attachment

Yamas Principles of social conduct

CPSIA information can be obtained
at www.ICGtesting.com
Printed in the USA
FSOW01n1708310317
32457FS